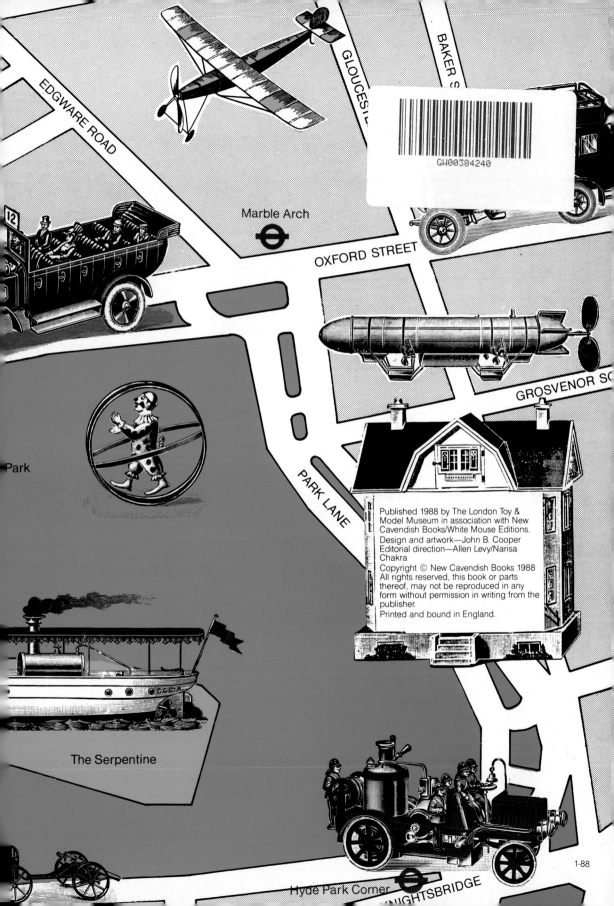

EDGWARE ROAD

GLOUCES

BAKER S

Marble Arch

OXFORD STREET

GROSVENOR S

12

Park

PARK LANE

Published 1988 by The London Toy &
Model Museum in association with New
Cavendish Books/White Mouse Editions.
Design and artwork—John B. Cooper
Editorial direction—Allen Levy/Narisa
Chakra

Printed and bound in England.

The Serpentine

C.C.C.N

Hyde Park Corner

KNIGHTSBRIDGE

1-88

GW00384240

This text has been edited from the introduction to a catalogue that accompanied the London Toy & Model Museum's major touring exhibition of Australia in 1983.

The serious collection and study of toys has gone on for many years and it would be true to say that in the main it has concentrated on pre-twentieth century toys, principally dolls, dolls houses and wooden and paper toys whose production did not primarily spring from the industrial revolution. The metal, factory produced and predominantly mechanical toy that arose in the mid-nineteenth century (coinciding with the birth of large factories capable of producing the piece parts necessary for these toys) has, surprisingly, been comparatively neglected until the last twenty-five years, and it was this type of toy that formed the basis of the LONDON TOY & MODEL MUSEUM.

The LONDON TOY & MODEL MUSEUM came into being through the interaction of three people, Allen Levy, Narisa Chakrabongse and David Pressland. The events leading to the formation of the museum had an interesting symmetry. Allen Levy was and is a long-time collector of toy and model trains and published the first major illustrated review of the subject 'A Century of Model Trains' in 1974. Real railways were actively mirrored through toys and models throughout their history and it was this historical rather than aesthetic approach that provided the spur to both his collection and book.

David Pressland's approach was entirely aesthetic and to this end he chose the Victorian and Edwardian eras as his subject. Over some fifteen years he has assembled one of the great international collections of toys of this period with a particular emphasis on German-made items. (Germany was predominant in the world of toy-making until the Second World War.) David Pressland wrote, and Allen Levy's company New Cavendish Books, published what has become accepted as the classic work on the history of these toys entitled 'The Art of the Tin Toy', in 1976.

The credos behind these two major collections is best conveyed by extracts from the books written by their respective owners:

'My father's absence on service during the last war put paid to any claims I might have had to vast childhood memories of model railways. In fact, the nearest I came to owning a "proper" locomotive was an aunt's promise in 1946 to return from a trip to London with a Bassett-Lowke "Enterprise". In the event, she returned with a Dinky Toy Scot Car – perhaps the price induced amnesia, or she met a salesman who had yet to find his true vocation.

'Evacuation from London during the war, a first glimpse of the sea, and later, travels abroad were all experiences primarily rememberd for their close links with steam-powered railway journeys. Those impressions, together with the hours spent – or mis-spent – at various London termini watching the great expresses come and go, were enough to form the basis of a life-long interest in railways – both prototype and make-believe.

'In the early 1960's, my interest in collecting model trains was confined to a few models typical of the railways I had known, but my curiosity was soon to take me down the long tunnel, away from my own nostalgia and into a world of model railways which existed long before my time or recollection.

'In early 1968 I became (in retrospect, quite by accident) a co-founder and for some three years a Director of Bassett-Lowke (Railways) Limited (a company formed primarily to market new lines in association with the original Bassett-Lowke company at Northampton). During that rather extraordinary departure in my career I travelled with the company's exhibition on the famous yet commercially ill-fated "Flying

Scotsman" Tour of the U.S.A. in 1969 from Boston down to Houston . . . a *folie de grandeur* on a magnificent scale. That period saw the last attempt to breathe life into the model railway department of Bassett-Lowke in so far as it concerned the Northampton factory (although industrial modelling, including railway projects, is still a major activity there).

'These years also saw the final production of the gauge 0 "Mogul" series which had lasted in one form or another for some forty-five years.

'When my commercial involvement with the company ceased, my interest in model trains was directed towards the re-establishment of my former collection, an interest spurred by my having witnessed a whole generation of buried treasure pass through Bassett-Lowke Railways' premises housed with Steam Age at Cadogan Street in London.'
Allen Levy 'A Century of Model Trains' 1974.

'David Pressland is by profession a veterinary surgeon, and a highly successful one. His other consuming interest is the study and collection of tin toys, especially those manufactured before 1914. To the pursuit of this interest, he brings both aesthetic appreciation and the discipline of a trained scientific mind, attributes which are very much in evidence in his superb account of "The Art of the Tin Toy". The author approaches the subject of tin toys and their collection from the standpoint of a perfectionist, and it is hardly surprising to learn that one of his life-long ambitions has been to own the best one hundred tin toys from the years before the First World War.'
Publisher's introduction: 'The Art of the Tin Toy' 1976.

The ring was closed by Narisa Chakrabongse, whose father, Prince Chula, and uncle, Prince Bira, shared a great interest in toys and models and were regular customers of Bassett Lowke Limited. A rare Märklin aeroplane which miraculously survived in a cupboard in a damp cellar in Bangkok for over 65 years, now forms part of David Pressland's collection. Narisa Chakrabongse also inherited the ERA racing car, Romulus, raced by her famous uncle Prince Bira and, between races, it is housed at the Museum along with its memorabilia.

Narisa Chakrabongse is also a keen collector of bears in all their forms and, as befits a museum situated in Paddington, they form a significant part of the collection.

In October 1980 a possible building some five minutes walk from Paddington station in West London was found and on May 12, 1982, the museum was opened, and has rapidly been acclaimed as one of the finest of its kind in the world.

It is interesting that London now has two major toy museums, the Bethnal Green Museum of Childhood in the east with its superlative collection of dolls, dolls houses and non-mechanical toys, and the LONDON TOY & MODEL MUSEUM in the west. Despite the fact that England was by no means the cradle of the toy industry, it nevertheless boasts some of the finest toy and model museums in the world. Thus it is wholly appropriate that this first major toy exhibition in Australia should come from England.

'The toy is a child's first introduction to art', wrote Baudelaire and, while this ubiquitous sage can be accused of leaving the world an epigram too many, his observation in this context is entirely apposite.

Toys, like any other creative process are good, bad, interesting or dull, worthy of preservation or not. Unlike the world of the more established arts, however, there was until recently no recognised body of opinion (or learning) waiting in the wings to give its judgement on this toy object or that.

Toys, like many of the new collectables (other than artificial collectables, namely those produced solely for 'collecting') go through two distinct phases. Firstly, they have a prime use, in this case to amuse, distract and/or educate children. In their second lives they become objects of study and research and form part of that total body of material that is handed down from generation to generation as a representation of what was deemed aesthetic, inventive or merely nostalgic at that particular time.

Until recently, toys, in the main, were treated as disposable ephemera in that when their first use was past they were discarded and merely retained subconsciously as childhood memories. Perhaps the exceptions were those toys which had a human or animal form, principally dolls and from c 1902 onwards the teddy bear, which were either handed on to succeeding generations or kept for emotional reasons. Humanity rules in the toy kingdom in that it is all right to scrap a car or train but a bear or doll . . .!

The problem with all conservation is the destiny of the objects after the original owner's and/or collector's life. If the subject has established itself as one of wide public interest or the establishment deem it worthy or important, then in many countries, museums will take on such collections even though they are peripheral to the main objects of the museum. In such a fashion the Bethnal Green Museum in London is part of the Victoria and Albert Museum of the Decorative Arts rather than an institution in its own right. If the collection is not so acquired, then it is usually sold, nowadays at auction, and thereby redistributed to other younger collectors in the field. However, a restriction in this process has been the escalation of price in the world of toys, turning younger collectors to more contemporary items and ones within their financial reach.

It is at this point that the need for a permanent exhibition area becomes important to a subject, for not only does it expose the subject to a far wider section of the population, but it also becomes the centre for a pooling of ideas and further research. Such a time has now arrived in Europe and America and with synchronicity at work several major museums are planned over the next few years. All collectors are amateur curators and run their own private museums, and it is these people scattered throughout the world who have saved many seemingly insignificant items from extinction — future generations might well thank them for their conscious or unconscious foresight.

One irony of the type of toys that are displayed in this exhibition is that they were conceived as adult interpretations of what the youthful mind would find attractive or constructive, etc. The decision to acquire them would often also be made by an adult and only when they finally reached the hands of their rightful recipients was their success or failure as playthings determined.

A further irony exists in that the less the toy was played with the greater its value to the contemporary collector. Furthermore, those toys which did not sell well and presumably did not reflect the tastes of the times, have an enhanced rarity and curiosity value which often puts them at an extraordinarily high premium.

In the collector's reassessment of these objects a further time warp takes place in that he or she invests the toy with a mature mind's interpretation of what it meant to own the toy as a child. The impulse to collect toys, while perhaps starting from a desire to recover the simplicity of childhood invariably proceeds to objects of which the collector has no childhood memories, as they were made long before his time or recollection. Another more simplistic but nonetheless relevant spur to the toy collector is the 'I never had one as a child' syndrome. This process was evidenced in West Germany in the 1960s and 1970s, when the demand for 1930s toy trains started its meteoric rise.

Although toys in the broadest sense can be found in antiquity, the period in which they unquestionably came to reflect popular taste and customs was that which coincided with the rise of the industrial revolution and with it a relatively affluent urban middle class with progressively more time for leisure in both childhood and adult life. Toys in some form or other became an almost universal part of children's lives in the developed world in the 1920s, and this coincided with the next great leap forward in technology, namely mass machine production rather than labour intensive methods.

Without question the over-riding validity of toys as objects worthy of preservation and study resides in their ability to be both popular art objects of their time and in many instances surprisingly accurate records of past life-styles, design and form. Dolls reveal the ever changing field of fashion, while trains bear testimony to the liveries and shapes of railway equipment which has long since disappeared. Elaborate dolls houses can reveal in miniature the domestic scenarios of past generations in the most intimate detail.

Once again, in extremely broad terms, toys also reflect the essentially sexist nature of parents' attitudes to their children. Until very recent times girls would receive toys that bore all the marks of their intended roles as housewives and mothers, whereas boys' toys would reflect science, engineering, wars and all those echoes of future 'manly' pursuits.

Aside from dolls and soft toys, by far and away the most prolific toy image is that relating to images of transportation. The materials used for their construction can be broadly broken down almost like the ages of man.

Firstly, there was the wooden age from the middle ages onwards. This was followed in the mid-nineteenth century by tin, at first hand-painted and then more dramatically printed, as chromolithography and offset printing were married with the advent of Welsh-made tinplate. Virtually unique to America was the iron age reflected in cumbersome, and to the European eye, ugly cast iron toys which lasted from the mid-nineteenth century right through to the Second World War. In the late 1930s various zinc alloys became widely used in toy manufacture in conjunction with high pressure die-casting techniques which were perfected in the United States. This led to Tootsie Toys in America, Dinky Toys in England and in the post-Second World War period to Lesney, Corgi and myriad other concerns making miniature transportation models. The post-Second World War period can equally be termed the Plastic Age, and once again the perfection of high pressure injection moulding machines led to massive production runs of lower unit costs which virtually ousted the metal toy, certainly from the cheap end of the market.

The majority of the exhibits in A CENTURY OF TOYS are drawn from the metal and tin periods because it is here that the dust has begun to settle on the times in which they were made, thus giving them historical perspective and a clearer opportunity to evaluate them.

There is little doubt that in twenty or thirty years time a similar exhibition will give great emphasis to the space toys of the 1950s and 1960s. By then they will have taken on an antiquity hardly thought possible today.

Reference is made throughout to both toys and models. It can be said that whereas many toy manufacturers who thought they were producing a model were in fact producing a toy, the opposite is rarely the case. If one had to distinguish between the model and toy, it is that the former aims at verisimilitude and does not primarily demand of its owner the exercise of imagination, whereas the latter sidesteps the issue of accuracy and scale, being more concerned with suggestion, leaving the gap between fact and fiction to be closed by the imagination of the beholder.

Perhaps national characteristics were in play in that England became the birthplace of the model whereas in America and the rest of Europe makers were not so concerned with models until the late 1920s. Thus the Victorian ethic struck deep into the nursery, particularly in so far as boys were concerned and, indeed, Frank Hornby's Meccano empire was founded on the ethos that serious and educational play would lead to the formation of the empire-building spirit.

Over all these periods the one common factor has been the fascination in reducing the real world through miniature objects, in the first instance so that children can control and own elements of the real world in a domestic setting, and latterly as objects that can be collected in a similar setting. Today the distinction between a toy and a collector's item has become very blurred, particularly with road vehicles and trains.

Having touched on the manufacturing processes, one is led inevitably to the manufacturers themselves. The toy industry is peculiar in that, while toys in the main are an industrial process, they nonetheless have always been geared to fashion and novelty. This aspect of the business required toy manufacturers to be a combination of visionary, engineer, salesman and prudent businessman. Over the history of the toy industry, which has been more casualty prone than most, it is easy to see that the omission of any of these facets could lead to the toy-maker's demise.

Of all the great toy manufacturers, only Marklin and Lehmann in Germany have survived from the late nineteenth century until today. Virtually all the other companies that have come and gone in the intervening periods were started by strong-willed entrepreneurs who either ran out of steam, money or failed to bring on adequate successors.

The first great toy-makers of Europe were unquestionably those of Southern Germany, mainly centred around the clock-making areas of Bavaria. Nuremberg was to become the centre of the German toy industry in the early part of the nineteenth century. Manufacturers such as Hess started around 1826, Märklin in 1859, Bing in 1865, Planck in 1866, Schoenner in 1875, Gunthermann in 1877, Lehmann in 1881 and Carette in 1886.

In France, firms such as F. Martin, Radiguet and G. Dessin arose in the 1880s. Britain assumed a lofty role in this upsurge, becoming one of the largest markets for toys and later, models from the Continent. This reflected the relative affluence of Britain in her heyday, but her great Victorian factories were not attuned to anything as flippant as toy-making. In the field of model trains, Britain was totally predominant in the mid-nineteenth century and with hindsight one can see that the train was to become in Britain what later the aeroplane would become in the United States. Reflecting the Victorian taste for engineering were such firms as Clyde and Stevens Model Dockyards in the 1860s and Bassett-Lowke from 1899 onwards. A more general toy-maker, later one of the world's predominant toy soldier manufacturers, was William Britains who began manufacturing in 1860. In 1901 Frank Hornby founded Meccano which in the 1920s would spawn Hornby Trains and a decade later, Dinky Toys.

In America the toy industry grew up in the New England area, in many instances founded on the skills of the immigrant tinsmiths from the Bristol area in England. Many toy factories sprung up in the early 1830s and by 1838 Francis, Field & Francis had a sizeable factory in Philadelphia. George W. Brown & Company produced the first recorded American clockwork toys in 1856. During the 1860s and 1870s, the factories of Althorf Bergmann & Company, Hull & Stafford, James Fallows, Edward Ives and Stevens & Brown were all in full production. America's most illustrious toy train maker, Lionel started production in 1900.

The Japanese toy industry became discernible in the early 1930s, and like so much of Japanese production in other fields in that period, a large percentage was pure plagiarism mainly at the expense of the Germans. When a Japanese firm turned its attention to the British train market they chose one of the most obscure and least successful ranges to copy. Perhaps they calculated that this firm was least able to bring legal action against them. Very little is known about Japanese manufacturers in the pre-Second World War period. Even in the post-war period when Japan took over from Germany as the world's principal toy-maker, only the names of such firms as Alps, Asahi or Bandai (founded in 1948-50) are known rather than any details of their companies. No doubt this problem is being worked on by contemporary historians, but no definitive book on this subject appears to be imminent.

It is worth recalling at this point a chapter from 'The Art of the Tin Toy' entitled 'Tin Toys for Everyone 1918-1939 – A Mirror of the Modern World':

'With the exception of Georges Carette and Jean Schoenner, the first of whom went out of business in 1917 and the second around 1906, the large German tin toy manufacturers recommenced production soon after the end of the First World War. Many of the immediate post-war toys were reproductions or slightly modified variations of pre-1914 toys. Karl Bub appeared to take over some of Carette's tools and produced several toy cars under the "Karl Bub" trademark which were exact copies of the Carette originals.

'Around 1920, a completely new series of toys began to appear, lighter in quality, less complex, and thus cheaper to produce than their Edwardian predecessors. Until this time toys had been designed and sold purely for their visual appearance and for their appeal to parent and child alike: but with the introduction in 1923 of the Citroen range, toys began to be sold for the first time with the express purpose of influencing a child's mind, in this case towards believing that Citroen was *the* maker of cars. Just as in the early 1900s, toy trains started to become model trains, and scale assumed a greater importance with every year, so, with the introduction of Citroen toys, a similar development took place in the world of toys.

'Construction kits became *a la mode*, and in England in the 1930s Meccano cars and planes were introduced, although they never achieved anything like the success of the original Meccano. The Citroen chassis and Märklin constructional series, appeared to be popular both at home and abroad. The 1930s also saw the rise of highly stylised design, a trend that was to become commonplace in tin toys of the post-Second World War era.'

Politically the 1930s were dominated by one man, Adolf Hitler, and his influence even cast its shadow over the nursery floor. Politics were to have a profound effect on proprietorship and many Jewish-owned firms disappeared, while in contrast companies like Lineol, Hausser and, to a lesser extent, Tipp prospered by pandering to and indeed cultivating the interest of the young in all things military. From the earliest days of the European tin toy industry America had been the largest export market − for instance, before 1914 about 65% of all Gunthermann's production was exported to the United States. A change occurred in the 1920s and 1930s, when for the first time American-made tin toys were exported to Europe in significant numbers, notably Kingsbury cars, Marx novelty toys and Lionel trains.

As we move further into the computer age, what has become apparent is the compression of childhood into a very narrow band, strangely echoing a similar though less happy phenomenon of Victorian times among lower-middle class and working-class children. Today, however, it is not the prospect of being

apprenticed to a chimney sweep that threatens the 7-year-old, but rather the intrusion of toys progressively linked to the mass media thereby squeezing out that element of fantasy and individuality so much in evidence in the toys exhibited here.

Models have become virtually the sole province of adults and few manufacturers today are abashed about this in their advertising. Although with expensive toys and dolls this was probably always the case, it was less overt and few early catalogues would have been aimed so specifically at the adult market. It seems as if in earlier times we needed an excuse to play (i.e. children), the work ethic being paramount, but today play or leisure is deemed a right and a necessity.

The objects of play of earlier times are now sufficiently distant to merit this type of retrospective exhibition and the very existence of such museums as the LONDON TOY & MODEL MUSEUM. It is hoped that the discovery by Australians of these items will shed further light on the technological and cultural roots of the 'new' country.

Allen Levy
London

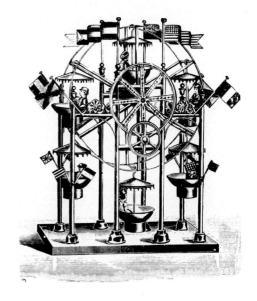

The London Toy & Model Museum was first opened to the public in May 1982. It was originally housed at 23 Craven Hill, a fine mid-Victorian building which formed one of the pavilions of three adjoining houses. In 1984, the museum was extended to take in no 21 Craven Hill together with the garden area.

No. 23 was in private occupation from about 1860 until the early 1950s at which time it became a language school. The house became derelict in 1979 and remained so until the opening of the museum.

The museum's permanent exhibition is based on the founders' private collections and has been supplemented by many important loans and donations.

General condition of the building in 1981

23 Craven Hill in 1981

Site meeting prior to purchase

The Clockwork Café

This area includes memorabilia associated with the White Mouse Garage, a famous historic racing team of the 1930s formed by H.R.H. Prince Chula Chakrabongse of Thailand. His daughter is one of the founders of the museum and the connection with models is illustrated in two superb Bassett-Lowke items, namely the live steam-powered $2\frac{1}{2}''$ gauge 'Cock o' the North' and an electric-powered liner 'Europa'. Both of these were in the possession of Prince Chula and his cousin, Prince Bira, who, in addition to being a successful racing driver, was a model railway enthusiast of some note. Both Princes were enthusiastic customers of Bassett-Lowke.

The most famous surviving family item of this period is the ERA (English Racing Automobile) 'Romulus' and in 1987 the car was removed from the museum in order to prepare it for its return to Thailand after a fifty year absence. There it took part in a special vintage car event at the Pattaya International Circuit being driven by its owner, Narisa Chakrabongse. When the car returns from Thailand it will be housed at Donnington.

One of the major themes of the museum is the conservation and operation of vintage and contemporary model railways. A showcase on the west wall of the café area displays superb examples of Bassett-Lowke's offerings provide a foretaste of the fine model train collection within the museum. A unique half-model of an ex-Southern Railway 'Lord Nelson' also depicts the work of this company as does a model of a Bengal Nagpur National Railway, Beyer Garratt built for Bassett-Lowke by Stanley Beeson in 1927. A fine model of the battleship 'Princess Elizabeth' in the scale of $1''/16'$ by Norman A. Ough can be seen on the north wall.

Completion of the second phase of 21 and 23 Craven Hill, 1984

Completion of the first phase of the museum in 1982, front and rear

The Garden Area

The garden area of the museum represents a unique facility in that it is the only open air area in any museum in a major capital in which working model railways operate throughout the year. The railways range from a 7¼" gauge railway hauling children (using battery-operated locomotives during the week and a steam locomotive on most Sundays) to gauge 2½", gauge 1 and gauge 0 scenic railways that are operated by steam, clockwork or electric locomotives. On the last Sunday of every month visitors may bring their own locomotives to run on the museum's tracks. Members of certain approved model railway societies may obtain passes to run at more frequent intervals. Various special events are held in connection with the working railways such as GWR day, LNER day, LMS day and SR day.

The 2½" gauge electric railway is one of the few operational railways in this gauge on public display and its history is outlined on a large notice board outside the station nearest the main museum building. The museum maintains a large stud of working locomotives which probably cover more scale miles per annum than many of their full-sized counterparts.

Of particular note are three locomotives built by F. Wrighton one of the foremost gauge 1 builders of his time and these may be seen in the working locomotive

Annual Peter Bull Teddy Bears Picnic, July

Boating Pond and Sunday steam service on the garden railway

showcase outside the main train room. A clock indicating the times of operation of live steam gauge 1 is attached to the veranda on the main bridge. All the museum's working models are maintained in the museum's own workshops and our staff would be glad to offer advice on the construction and maintenance of garden railways between running sessions.

The museum is fortunate in having a large boating pond (which also contains several large carp who have survived many winters under ice). They do not object to being fed and their favourite area is the north-east corner of the pond, nearest the café terrace. Children or adults may bring non-petrol driven boats for sailing on the pond at any time.

The vintage Orton & Spooner children's roundabout is in operation from April till October. This particular example was completed in 1920 but the design dates back to the turn of the century. The peacock chairs were required to be carved by apprentices as part of their training.

A 1947 Leyland P1 open-topped double decker bus, formerly owned by the Southport Corporation, is housed in the garden and children may sit in the cab and also go on both decks of the bus subject to it being used by groups as a picnic area.

'Mallard' entering Greenly Road station

Take a miniature ride to Paris on the boat train

Gauge 1 in the garden

English wooden doll
in original costume, c. 1789

Special Exhibition Gallery

This area is devoted to special exhibitions and temporary loans. Special exhibitions within the museum have included 'Dinky Toys — Fifty Years', 'American Kit made Cars of the 1950s', 'On Guard' and the 'Minic' exhibitions. One of the most famous temporary exhibitions was 'Baywest City' which was installed in the museum for 18 months. Our permanent display of space toys, motorcycles and plastic kits may be seen in this room. The area behind the special exhibition space will be arranged as an activity room and video theatre for small children and will open in 1988.

Dollshouse and Doll Display

The doll collection was assembled by Constance Eileen King on behalf of the museum and attempts to represent a broad cross-section of dates, manufacturers and materials. Materials range from wax, wood, leather

Trio of Nora Wellings
dolls, c. 1935, British

and felt to bisque and the collection includes such manufacturers as Bru, Jumeau, Lenci and Simon and Halbig.

The small display of dollshouses includes German-made Victorian villas and a dollshouse representing Queen Elizabeth's famous miniature house made by Triang in 1936. In front of the dollshouse section is an extraordinary model of Green's General Store based on an actual shop. It contains commercially-made miniatures which very accurately convey the flavour of small town American life. Everything from vegetables to toboggans could be purchased there.

Early Wooden Toys are displayed in a showcase opposite the doll section and are arranged around a superb wooden fort made in the Erzgeberg region of Germany about 1830. It has survived virtually intact with the original box top.

Klammer and Reinhardt character doll, c. 1912, German

Die-cast, Plastic and Tin Transport Collection
1930 to the Present Day

This room houses a changing exhibition area which illustrates the broad diversity of miniature transport models made in virtually every country of the industrialized world over the last fifty years. Exhibits are in the main arranged nationally with the names of the manufacturer and the flag representing the country as indicators. Names such as Dinky Toys, Lesney, Tecno, Solido, Minic and lesser-known marques are well represented.

Several examples of larger scale plastic and tin cars of the '50s and '60s are included in this area.

Dinky Toy Golden Jubilee special exhibition, 1983

Early Matchbox 'Yesteryear' toys, c. 1960

Flying Scotsman Showcase

The main theme of this showcase is the depiction of the famous locomotive and its train through the eyes of various model makers. The centrepiece is a superb 5″ gauge model of an A3 Pacific by Perrier of c. 1960. The model has three cylinders as in the original. Another theme of the showcase deals with various aspects of British locomotive design, culminating with a 5″ gauge model of the last steam locomotive built for British Railways, the 'Evening Star". This model, built by Mr. Lowe, typifies the widespread skills existing among amateur British model engineers and, in many ways, it reflects the legacy of Britain's industrial heritage.

A model of particular significance in this showcase is a Midland Railway 4-4-0 'Beatrice' made by Bernard Miller for W. S. Norris' legendary 0 gauge railway.

The Bassett-Lowke Shop

W. J. Bassett-Lowke started his model business in Northampton at the turn of the century and he can be regarded as being the founder of commercially-made model railways in this country. Under the direction of himself and Henry Greenly, models of great accuracy were made in England and Germany for the British market. These products were primarily in gauge 0, 1, 2 and $2\frac{1}{2}$″ gauge and a good cross-section of these models are displayed in the shop and the showcase in the café area. Bassett-Lowke were also in the forefront of miniature garden railways so popular with the landed gentry before the First World War and a superb example of a Northampton-made 'Royal Scot' in $7\frac{1}{4}$″ gauge and originally owned by the Earl of Downshire is on display.

Although model railways were the mainstay of the business, ships and boats were another major facet of their work and these range from the superb models commissioned by Cunard, P & O and all the great steamship companies to simple launches and yachts for sailing on the local pond. One of the finest examples of the latter type is an electrically-powered model of the Nord Deutsche Lloyd 'Europa' (previously the 'Bremen')

purchased by Prince Chula Chakrabongse and on display in the café.

Bassett-Lowke was also very interested in all modern technology and design, commissioning the famous architect Charles Rennie Mackintosh to design two houses for him in and near Northampton. Examples of his interest in graphic design can be seen in the covers of his very distinctive catalogues, some of which are on display.

The Meccano Shop

The Meccano Shop endeavours to recreate the atmosphere of the typical small shop that sold Meccano products over the years. Invariably a shade untidy, the excitement of the red-boxed Hornby trains was unmistakable. Meccano Ltd, founded in 1901, was Britain's most illustrious toy-making company spawning the Meccano system, Hornby Trains, Dinky Toys and later Hornby Dublo Trains. Towards the end of Hornby 0 gauge in the later 1930s, Hornby Trains were taking on a more scale appearance and all the major examples of these scale trains may be seen in the shop: the 'Schools' class, the 'L1', the 'County of Bedford', the LMS 'Compound' and the most famous of all, 'The Princess Elizabeth'.

An interesting scientific Meccano set is displayed in the shop and it reflects the tremendous expansion in educational toys that took place at the beginning of the century. Meccano in particular enabled most of the engineering feats to be made in whole or part on the kitchen table. This system coupled with the legendary "Meccano Magazine" which ran almost continually from 1916 to 1981 represents a unique interaction between a commercial toy company and its public.

A small display of Dinky toys may be seen but the majority of the collection is to be found in the transport section.

The Craven Hill Toyshop

A broad selection of popular toys and games including British-made boats.

Bassett-Lowke and Meccano Shop reconstructions

Flying Scotsman showcase

The Animal House

The range of toys produced in the last 150 years was extremely varied and animals of both inanimate and mechanical form have been popular with children of all ages and both sexes. A cross-section is displayed here with a special emphasis on mechanical teddy bears in the cabinet to the left of the door.

On the right wall is a very comprehensive collection of Lineol and Elastolin animals including some rare examples of 1930s dinosaurs.

At the end of the gallery, a large contemporary English bear named, Evelyn Paugh, is seated in a 1916 $\frac{1}{4}$ scale Cadillac presented by that company to the King of Thailand. The King then gave the car to his nephew and it is now on loan to the museum by its current owner, Narisa Chakrabongse.

The centre display contains a selection of postcards with the theme of children and toys. Of particular note are two pictures depicting the summary execution of a teddy bear charged with being a traitor during the First World War (the Teddy Bear is claimed to have originated with the German firm of Margarete Steiff), an early example of political propaganda entering the nursery.

'Evelyn Paugh' in a $\frac{1}{4}$ scale electric powered Cadillac made by Cadillac for the King of Thailand in 1916

A selection of the museum's tinplate air fleet

Some of the museum's racers and record breakers —

'Brooklands'

Brooklands was a famous racing circuit in the inter-war years. The toy and model racing cars arranged on the banking indicate the popularity of this exotic machinery with the toy makers' youthful customers. A good collection of record-breaking cars is also exhibited. Brooklands was also an airfield and some of the museum's squadrons circle above this display.

The Nursery

The entrance to the nursery simulates a giant dollshouse and the first right-hand window contains the Peter Bull Teddy Bear collection, and the Joan Dunk Teddy Bear collection. A cross-section model of a Victorian town house, not dissimilar to the one in which the museum is housed, can be seen at the end of this passage. In it are arranged contemporary artefacts which recreate the essential feeling of the 'upstairs-downstairs' environment of a Victorian household.

The main nursery has been designed around the original cast iron kitchen range of the house and contains nursery items ranging from the later nineteenth century through to relatively modern times. From paper theatres to Bing model bathrooms, from the traditional rocking horse to the ubiquitous Paddington Bear. The exhibition and arrangement of this nursery is

The nursery is arranged around the original stove of the house dating from c. 1860

Schuco mechanical walking bears, c. 1909, German

20

German Bavarian wooden ark and 90 pairs of animals

constantly changing as would be the case with this type of room.

The Soldier Cabinet

The soldier cabinet represents a further important loan collection and illustrates the seemingly endless variety offered by such German and English makers as Heyde, Britains and Elastolin. The figures were predominantly metal and several charming non-military sets are displayed here. The Great Race to the Pole was one such set and was originally contained in a single box.

Toys made during the Second World War are also on display in this cabinet and few of these survived as they were commandeered for scrap in order to serve the very war effort they depicted. The makers of such toys were Tipp, Hausser and Lineol.

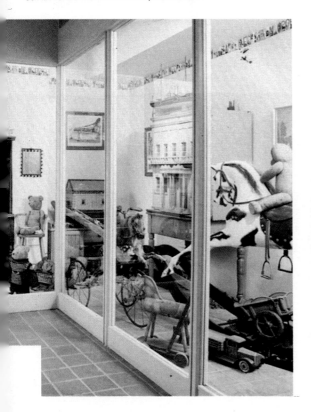

Paddington Bear as seen on TV

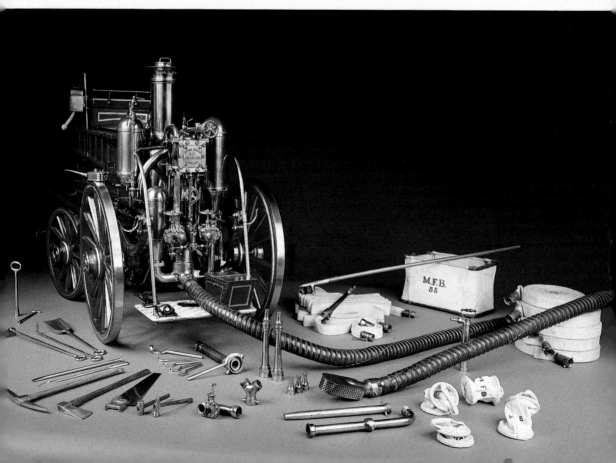

The Penny Toy Cabinet

At the top of the stairs can be seen a small but good collection of penny toys, those small cheap but delightful toys produced in vast quantities around the turn of the century and sold at street fairs and markets. The range of invention displayed is quite remarkable and these toys show what was available at the lower end of the market in terms of price. Once again Germany was the main supplier of such toys which have a close affinity with the long-standing manufacture of Christmas ornaments.

Union Toys may be seen on the top left. Several American cast iron horse-drawn fire engines are at the bottom of the showcase, some of which are relatively recent reproductions.

On the right of this cabinet is a small but comprehensive collection of stationary steam engines by Doll, Marklin, Bing, Carette, Stuart Turner etc. These engines symbolize the prime sources of power in the late nineteenth century and also the relative lack of

Bing horsedrawn fire engine, 1904 German

Fire Engine Showcase

This showcase contains models and toys reflecting the excitement and drama of the fire. The centrepiece is a superlative Shand Mason Salesman's demonstration model built by Thomas Coates in 1888. This model is surrounded by a collection of classic toy fire engines including a fine live-steam horse-drawn fire engine by Bing of 1904. An extremely rare American fire engine by

safety legislation concerning playthings at that time.

At the far end of this gallery is a loan collection of buses whose manufacture ranges from Germany to China.

Opposite the fire engine cabinet in small wall displays is a collection of lead flats and metal miniatures showing the diversity of the toy maker's art. The majority of these items were manufactured in Germany.

Thomas Coates builders model of Shand Mason fire engine and all accessories, 1888 English

JEP Rolls Royce clockwork, c. 1930 French

DL Renault Sedanca de Ville, cw, c. 1920 Spanish

Citroën B 14 Coupé, c. 1929 French

Wyandotte Cord, c. 1937 American

American Model Toys Jaguar XK 140 mid-1960s American

Mercedes Benz 300 SE, c. 1968 Japanese

The Tin Toy Room

Opposite the optical showcase is a small display of *aeronautical toys* including several particularly rare Bing flying models manufactured during the early days of real flight. An especially unusual and fine Lockheed Monoplane made in Japan during the 1930s and a Tipp R100 airship should be noted. One of the best pre-war construction kits is illustrated by the made-up Junkers by Marklin.

The *Motor Car* section includes representatives of virtually every major toy manufacturer and an early Carette tonneau may be one of the earliest toy representations of an early vehicle and dates from 1890. A steam tricycle probably pre-dates Benz's first road vehicle as quite often the toymaker's imagination ran ahead of real events. Hand-enamelled and lithographed cars right through to the 1930s are displayed here and of particular note are JEP's Rolls-Royce and a large Renault Sedanca de Ville by the Spanish maker DL.

A collection of the museum's novelty toys on view /
in the animal house and the Tin Toy Room

A selection from the museum fleet in cast iron and tin ‒

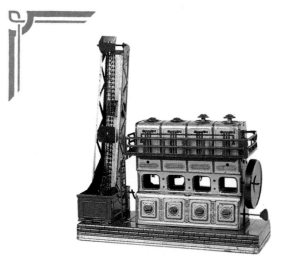

George Levy diesel-operated dredging machine, cw, c. 1930 German

Betal Trolley Bus 1950 English

Marx Easter Bunny Train gauge 0, c. 1936 American

The boat section includes a particularly fine Carette steamer and one of the most spectacular early toy boats to have 'Surfaced' in recent years, namely the battleship 'La Plata' by Schoenner dating from 1895. The toy-like qualities of this vessel can be contrasted with the tinplate but almost scale quality of the 'Princess Cecilie' by Fleischmann which was probably made for a shipping company. Other aquatic toys of note are the Bing 'plunging pike' and the French-made Swimming Dog'.

A revolving display contains various novelty tin-toys including billiard players, walking races, various musicians and some Lehmann novelty toys. Two of the most notable toys are a magnificent example of Britains 'Walking race' including the finishing post and the mysterious Ball which has been demonstrated many times by the museum on television.

The street scene shows toys in a charming setting including a particularly fine example of an English wooden butchers shop, a stable and an excellent collection of steam rollers under the railway bridge. Various aeronautical toys also feature together with a parachute toy.

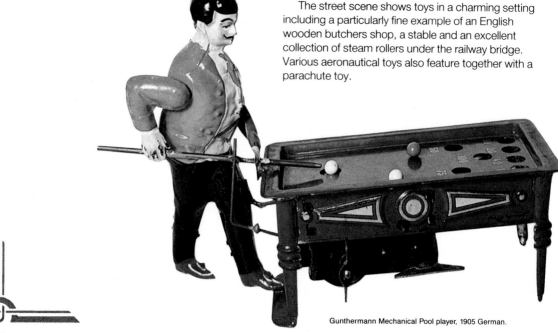

Gunthermann Mechanical Pool player, 1905 German.

Bing four-funnel Liner in almost perfect original condition, cw, c.1912 German

George Levy 'Rowing eight', c.1920 German

Marklin 'Linienschiff', cw, c.1923 German

Schoenner 'La Plata' twin-boilered live steam, c.1895 German

Lead flats commemorating the first German railway, c.1835 German

The Train Room

The train collection is broadly arranged in chronological order and attempts to illustrate the history of commercially made toys and models, which followed closely the development of real public railways from c.1828 (the opening of the Stockton and Darlington railway) onwards.

The history of toy and model railways is uniquely linked with the history of their full-sized counterparts. In no other area of transportation has the development of real technology been contemporaneously mirrored in miniature. Thus from the first appearance of the steam locomotive until its demise, in most parts of the world, in the mid-twentieth century, its styles, shapes and colours have been faithfully or amusingly captured in toys and models.

The display begins with artefacts and experimental models contemporary with the birth of 'railway mania', and continues with the products of both the great and obscure manufacturers, such illustrious names as the British Model & Electrical Company, Stevens and Clyde Model Dockyards, Bassett-Lowke, Marklin, Schoenner, Carette, Bing, etc. The viewer will find that a wide range of motive power was used for these models from live steam to child's 'push and pull' power. Even more various were the different gauges which had emerged by the turn of the century.

Although England was one of the major markets for commercially produced model railways and was at the forefront of the Industrial Revolution, it was by no means the cradle of their manufacture. That was undisputedly in Germany and in particular the clock-making regions of Bavaria in the South.

Radiguet for Stevens Model Dockyard 'Wellington', c.1895 French

Part of the tin-plate station collection

Britains Rotary Express, c. 1885 English

Carette Caledonian Railway advertising train, c. 1910 German

The Gauges

The evolution of the railway gauge, i.e. the width between the two inside faces of the rails was in real practice an adaptation of the plate ways on which early horse-drawn wagons ran.

The evolution of the model railway gauge was equally arbitrary and it was not until the late 1930s that any real attempt was made at international standardisation.

In most of the captions the arabic notation is used – G, O, 1, 2, 3, etc. These are given when they correspond to the manufacturer's catalogue descriptions. One anomaly should be explained, namely that Marklin's gauge 3 was in reality the equivalent of Bing's gauge 4. Furthermore some manufacturers often described their products' gauges in terms of inches, e.g. Schoenner as sold by Bassett-Lowke.

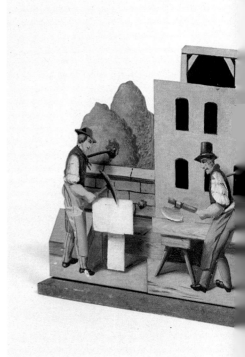

The showcases in this gallery are numbered in the panels above the lighting units.

Showcases I and II

These showcases illustrate the dawn of the model, both as an aid to industry (nos 7 and 11) and later as a plaything (the brass 'dribblers' nos 1-4) for the Victorian household. Of particular interest is no 9 which is a salesman's prototype model of a 2–4–0 Bury Type 'Nile', demonstrated to would-be purchasers by feeding in compressed air. The earliest dated railway item in the museum is the charming inkwell by C. Rowley dated 1853 and cigar holder in the form of a tender by the same manufacturer, dated 1847. These were products of 'railway mania' which gripped the public imagination in much the same way as did the aeroplane and moon rocket of later times. Note too that many companies were not exclusively toy or model makers. Thus optical and instrument makers might well turn their hand to locomotive modelling initially as a sideline to their main business.

By observing the various catalogues displayed in showcase I, you will note that many of these early British and French-made brass steam locomotives were very much the province of the rich. The average price was in the region of £5 – many times the multiple of a working man's weekly wage.

The majority of the models in these showcases are of British manufacture and they show a disregard for economy of manufacture both in weight and method of construction.

Trainee engineers were often made to build model

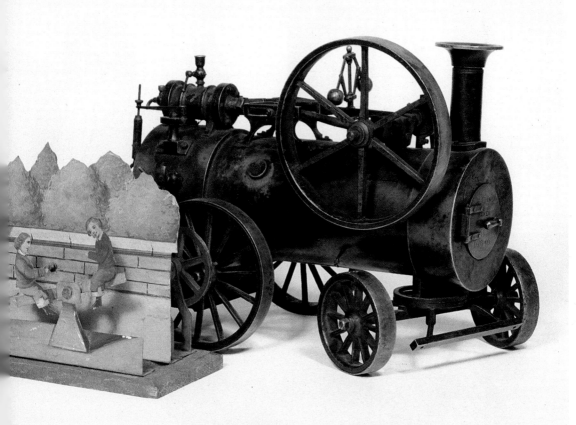

Woods portable engine, c. 1870 English. This forms part of the stationary steam engine display

steam engines. In some cases as in showcase II no 16 these exercises were theoretical. In others, e.g. in no 11 by David Puller they achieved a full working model which probably preceded the actual engine. As no example of this particular locomotive is preserved this model is the only three dimensional representation left to us.

These early models were invariably steam-powered with varying degrees of efficiency and safety. Note too the lack of protection for the 'driver', reflecting actual conditions at that time.

Opposite showcases I and II can be seen a display of Hornby gauge 0 equipment from the inter-war years.

Showcase III

This showcase contains some of the earliest examples of the first European tin toy trains whose manufacture arose as early as the 1860s by makers such as Lutz and Hess of Germany and FV of France. These hand-painted toys were relatively cheap when compared with their brass Victorian counterparts, and in

Schoenner American floor locomotive, cw, c. 1904 German

all cases they ran without tracks, propelled either by clockwork or pull and push power. By the turn of the century sophisticated lithographed printing on tin had become perfected and a superb example of a tin floor train is no 23 by Schoenner for the American market.

Most of the models depicted from showcase III to VI illustrate the work of the German manufacturers, particularly for the English market. Two engines of particular note may be seen in showcase VII, namely a gauge 3 Marklin Great Northern set and an extremely rare Schoenner 4–4–0 in similar gauge.

Showcase IX

This showcase is devoted to one of Britain's largest railway companies, the LNWR. (Remember, that until 1922 numerous regional railway companies operated throughout the British Isles. At that time they were amalgamated into the London North Eastern Railway (LNER), the London Midland Scottish (LMS),the Southern Railway (SR) and the Great Western Railway (GWR). In 1951 these in turn became British Railways (BR).) The LNWR was known as the Premier Line and

there can be little doubt that more models were made by all contemporary manufacturers of this railway's equipment than virtually any other. As may be observed from this display, the standard of tinplate rolling stock improved considerably from 1905 onwards and once again they are extremely interesting and often the only reminders of how trains actually looked at that time.

Showcase X

This showcase provides a cross-section of American model railway equipment. In America the electric train was unquestionably paramount both in terms of motive power and outline. The unique Hubley elevated railway (no 21) is one of the finest examples of such a toy known to exist.

Bing LSWR 'Adams Flyer' Gauge 3 live steam, c. 1903 German and Bing LSWR coach

Americans, as the world's first great consumer society, were very aware of design. If a train looked fast it *must* be fast. Consequently streamlining was introduced in a big way in the United States, producing some wonderfully elegant trains as a result.

Collecting trains in America has reached such a pitch that there is now a thriving industry in reproducing vintage trains and, indeed, in some cases new 'vintage' models which are not based on any originals have been invented to feed this market. A particularly fine example of this non-vintage 'vintage' train is the Hiawatha Standard gauge set by John Daniels of c.1975 (no 45).

Central Showcase

The base of the central showcase depicts a recreation of a typical electric gauge 0 railway of the 1930s principally using Marklin equipment. At right angles to this is an elevated figure-of-eight railway by Carette of c.1905, above which hangs a piece of Marklin track from one of the rarest elevated railways, the Barmen-Elberfield railway of c.1905.

The middle level of this showcase illustrates the development of 00 and HO railways which gained great popularity after the Second World War and also reflected the diminution in living areas in that period. Of particular interest in this section is a prototype of Hornby's 'Duchess of Atholl' in a presentation box. The production of this particular set was halted by the advent of the Second World War.

Above this level is a juxtaposition of the then and now of model railways and a layout of c.1902 can be seen alongside a model of Axford built in 4 mm scale built by Dave Rowe. The latter could be described as the current state of the art and it was the dream of all pioneer model railway enthusiasts to achieve standards of this nature.

On ascending the short flight of stairs, the display continues round the train room with showcases XI to XIV. The exhibits which range from approximately 1920 to 1980 reflect the gradual change from non-scale models to super detail. It also shows the transition in the main country of manufacture from Germany to Japan. Among this display are also interesting items manufactured in France, Italy, Russia and Britain.

Opposite the modern section is an area which is devoted to special displays of single manufacturer small gauge railways. This display changes from time to time and shows such makes as Trix, Fleischmann, Triang, etc.

The garden scene.

BIBLIOGRAPHY — Suggested further reading on toys and models

Ailen, Alistair: *Scraps,* exhibition catalogue, Bethnal Green Museum, London, 1977.

Altes Spielzeughaus Basel, Historisches Museum, Basle, 1973.

Aries, Philippe: *Centuries of Childhood,* Jonathan Cape, London, 1962.

Athletics, Sports, Games and Toys, London, October, 1895.

Bachmann, Fritzsch: *An Illustrated History of Toys,* Abbey Library, London, 1966.

Baecker, Carlernst: *Germany's Forgotten Toymakers,* Frankfurter Fachbuchhandlung Michael Kohl, 1982.

Bartok, Peter: *The Minic Book,* New Cavendish Books, London, 1987.

Bossi, Marco: Autohobby, Priuli & Verlacco, Ivrea, circa 1976.

Bing, Gebruder: German catalogues, 1906 and 1909; English, 1912.

Boehn, Max von: *Puppets and Automata,* Dover Reprints, New York, 1972.

Britains, William, Ltd.: 1954 catalogue reprinted by Britains Ltd., 1972.

Britains Toy and Model Catalogue, 1940, reprint, Almark Publications, London, 1972.

Burkij-Bartwlink, A.: *Antiek Speelgoed,* Van Dishoeck, Bussum, 1973.

Carette, George, The Great Toys of, reprint of 1911 trade catalogue, New Cavendish Books, London, 1976.

Chad Valley Ltd.: catalogues from 1897 to 1954.

Chapuis, A., and Droz, E.: *Les Automates,* Neuchatel, 1949.

Coleman, D., E. & E.: *The Collector's Encyclopedia of Dolls,* Robert Hale, London, 1970.
The Collector's Book of Dolls' Clothes, Robert Hale, London, 1976.

Cook, Olive: *Movement in Two Dimensions,* Hutchinson, London, 1963.

Culff, Robert: *The World of Toys,* Hamlyn, London, 1969.

Daiken, Leslie: *Children's Toys Throughout the Ages,* Spring Books, London, 1963.

Dean's Rag Book Company: catalogues from 1911 to 1938.

Ellis, Hamilton: *Model Railways, 1838-1939,* Allen & Unwin, London, 1962.
Everybody's Book of the Queen's Doll's House, published by *The Daily Telegraph,* London, 1924.

Foster, Michael: The Hornby Companion Series, Vol. 3, *Hornby Dublo Trains 1938-1964,* New Cavendish Books, London, 1980.

Fraser, Antonia: *A History of Toys,* Weidenfeld & Nicholson, London, 1966.

Freeman, Ruth: *American Dolls,* Century House, New York, 1952.

Fuller, Roland, and Levy, Allen: *The Bassett Lowke Story,* New Cavendish Books, London, 1984.

Gamage's Christmas Bazaar, 1913, reprint, David & Charles, Newton Abbott, 1974.

Garrett, John G.: *Model Soldiers, a Collector's Guide,* Seeley Service Co. Ltd., London, 1965.

Gottschalk, Lillian: *American Motor Toys,* New Cavendish Books, London, 1986.

Graebe, Chris & Julie: The Hornby Companion Series, Vol. 5, *The Hornby Gauge 0 System,* New Cavendish Books, London, 1985.

Green, Vivien: *English Dolls' Houses,* Batsford, London, 1955.
Family Dolls' Houses, G. Bell, London, 1973.

Greilsamer, Jacques and Azema, Bertrand: *Catalogue of Model Cars of the World,* Edita, Lausanne, and Patrick Stephens, London, 1967.

Grober, Karl: *Children's Toys of Bygone Days,* Batsford, London, 1928.

Hannas, Linda: *The English Jigsaw Puzzle,* Wayland Publishers, London, 1962.

Two Hundred Years of Jig Saw Puzzles, London, Museum Catalogue, 1968.

Hart, Louella: *Directory of British Dolls,* privately printed, USA, 1964.

Haskell, A., and Lewis, M.: *Infantillia. The Archaeology of the Nursery,* Dobson, London, 1971.

Hertz, Louis H.: *Messrs Ives of Bridgeport,* Mark Heber Co., USA, 1950.

Hillier, Mary: *Automata and Mechanical Toys,* Jupiter, London, 1976.

Hobbies Handbooks, Hobbies, Ltd., Norfolk, 1934-1940.

Hornby, Frank: *The Life Story of Meccano,* facsimile reprint of Meccano Magazine, 1932-1953, New Cavendish Books, London, 1976.

Howarth-Loomes, Bernard: *Victorian Photography,* Ward Lock, London, 1974.

Hughes, Bernard and Therle: *Collecting Miniature Antiques,* Heinemann, London, 1973.

Illustrated Sporting and Dramatic News, selected issues, London, 1887.

Jackson, Mrs. F. Nevil: *Toys of Other Days,* White Lion Reprint, London, 1976.

Jacobs, Flora Gill: *History of Dolls' Houses,* Scribners, New York, 1965.
Dolls' Houses in America, Scribners, New York, 1974.

Jacobs, Flora Gill and Faurholt, Estrid: *Dolls and Doll Houses.* Charles E. Tuttle, Rutland, USA, 1967.

Kelly, Dale: *Collecting Tin Toy Cars 1950-70,* Schiffer import, New Cavendish Books, USA, 1976.

King, Constance E.: *A Collector's History of Dolls,*
Robert Hale, London, 1977.
Price Guide to Antique Dolls, Antique Collectors
Club, Woodbridge, Suffolk, 1977.
Toys and Dolls for Collectors, Hamlyn, London, 1973.
Dolls and Dolls' Houses, Hamlyn, London, 1977.

Kurtz, Henry I., & Ehrlich, Burtt R.: *The Art of the Toy
Soldier,* New Cavendish Books, London, 1987.

Ladies Home Journal, New York, selected editions 1924
to 1926.

Latham, Jean: *Dolls' Houses. A Personal Choice,*
A. & C. Black, London, 1969.

Levy, Allen: *A Century of Model Trains,* New Cavendish
Books, London, 1974.

Love, Bert, and Gamble, Jim: The Hornby Companion
Series, Vol. 6, *The Meccano System and the Special
Purpose Meccano Sets,* New Cavendish Books,
London, 1986.

McKay, James: *Nursery Antiques,* Ward Lock Ltd.,
London, 1976.

MacClintock, Marshall and Innez: *Toys in America,*
Public Affairs Press, Washington, 1961.

McClinton, Katherine Morrison: *Antiques in Miniature,*
Scribners, New York, 1970.

Manduca, Joseph and Walker, Michael J.: Hornby
Companion Series, Vol. 7, *The Meccano Magazine
1916-1981,* New Cavendish Books, London, 1987.

Marklin: *Technical Toys in the Course of Time,* reprinted
catalogues, Hobby Haas, Frankfurt a. M., 1975.

Marshall Field Toy Catalogue, 1892-1893, edited by
Dale Kelley, Wallace Homestead Book Company,
Iowa, 1967.

Mateaux, C.L.: *Wonderland of Work,* Cassell, Petter,
Galpin & Co., London, 1883.

Mechanisches Spiel und Theater, catalogue, Stadt-
museum, Munich, 1972.

Maingot, Eliane: *Les Automates,* Hachette, Paris, 1959.

Moderne Kunst in Meister Holzschnitten, Richard Bong,
Munich, circa 1910.

Mogridge, G.S.: *Sergeant Bell and his Raree Show,*
Thomas Tegg, circa 1845.

Naegelsbach, Barbara Emde: *Antiquitaten-Spielzeug,*
Heyne, Munich, 1974.

Oberammergau Folk Museum Guide, published by the
Community of Oberammergau, 1963.

Ortman, Erwin: *The Collector's Guide to Model Tin
Figures,* Studio Vista, 1974.

Pearsall, Ronald: *Collecting Mechanical Antiques,*
David & Charles, Newton Abbot, 1973.

Powell, Rosamund Bayne: *The English Child in the
18th Century,* John Murray, London, 1939.

Prasteau, Jean: *Les Automates,* Grund, Paris, 1968.

Pressland, David: *The Art of the Tin Toy,* New Cavendish
Books, London, 1976.

Puppen & Spielzeug, No. 3, Stuttgart, 1977.

Quayle, Eric: *The Collector's Book of Children's Books,*
Studio Vista, London, 1971.

Randall, Peter: *The Products of Binns Road – A General
Survey,* The Hornby Companion Series, Vol. 1, New
Cavendish Books, London, 1977.

Reder, Gustav: *Clockwork, Steam and Electric. A
History of Model Railways,* Ian Allan, London, 1972.

Remise, Jacques, and Jean Fondin: *The Golden Age of
Toys,* Edita, Lausanne, 1967.

Richardson, Mike and Sue: *Dinky Toys and Modelled
Miniatures,* The Hornby Companion Series, Vol. 4,
New Cavendish Books, London, 1981.

Roe, F. Gordon: *The Georgian Child,* Phoenix,
London, 1961.

Roh, Juliane, and Hansmann, Claus: *Altes Spielzeug,*
Bruckmann, Munich, 1958.

Schiffer, Margaret: *Battery Toys,* New Cavendish Books,
import from Schiffer.

Schiffer, Herbert F. and Peter B.: *Miniature Antique
Furniture,* Livingston, USA, 1972.

Schiffer, N.: *Corgi Toys,* New Cavendish Books, import
from Schiffer.

Strong Museum, Margaret Woodbury, leaflet produced
by Lincoln First Bank of Rochester, New York.

Speaight, George: *The History of the English Toy
Theatre,* Studio Vista, London, 1967.

Tallis, David: *Musical Boxes,* Frederick Muller,
London, 1971.

Taranovskoi, N.V.: *Folk Toys of Russia,* 1968.

Teaching Toys, Norfolk Museum Service Booklet, 1975.

Thomas, D.B.: *The Origins of the Motion Picture,*
Science Museum, HMSO, London, 1964.

Tilley, Roger: *A History of Playing Cards,* Studio Vista,
London, 1973.
Playing Cards, Octopus, London, 1973.

Toller, Jane: *Antique Miniature Furniture,* Bell,
London, 1966.

Toy Trader and Fancy Goods Review, London, 1906
to 1960.

White, Gwen: *Dolls, Automata, Marks and Labels,*
Batsford, London, 1975.
Antique Toys and Their Background, Batsford,
London, 1971.

Whitehouse, F.R.B.: *Table Games of Victorian and
Georgian Days,* Priory Press, Royston, and Chad
Valley, Birmingham, 1971.

Wright, Geoff: *The Meccano Super Models,* The Hornby
Companion Series, Vol. 2, New Cavendish Books,
London, 1978.

INDEX OF TOY AND MODEL MANUFACTURERS ON VIEW IN THE MUSEUM

This index of manufacturers and brief description relate to those whose toys and models are on display in the museum. The location of where examples of such toys may be found is given in the brackets at the end of each entry.

TOY AND MODEL TRAINS

American Flyer – Founded 1907. American. The early trains were very similar to those of Ives and in 1928, American Flyer acquired Ives' stock. In 1915, electric models were introduced. In 1938 the firm was taken over by A.C. Gilbert before finally being taken over by Lionel in 1967. It was the only American manufacturer to produce a European outline model train. (Train Room). See also British Flyer.

Arcade – 1868-1946. American. Founded in Freeport, Illinois, the firm produced cast iron floor trains. (Train Room).

Aster – 1976-present day. Japanese. Originally manufacturers of office equipment, the firm extended its production principally to include gauge 1 steam locomotives in 1976. The firm has worked in association with *Fulgurex,* with the latter sponsoring models for the European and American markets. (Train Room).

Bar Knight – 1920s. British. Founded in Glasgow, Scotland, the firm produced a range of rather crude locomotives in electric and steam. (Train Room).

Bassett-Lowke Ltd – 1899-present day. British. The company was founded in 1899 by Wenman J. Bassett-Lowke. A simple catalogue was issued in 1901 and the first printed catalogue in 1902. Bassett-Lowke's meeting at the 1900 Paris Exhibition with Stefan Bing started his long association with the Nuremburg companies. Bassett-Lowke encouraged the German factories to produce near-scale models and as a consequence he may be considered to be the founder of model railways. Between the wars an increasing percentage of Bassett-Lowke's models were English-made. W.J. Bassett-Lowke died in 1953 and thereafter the company's model-train production declined, emphasis going to industrial and museum models. (Bassett-Lowke Shop, Train Room, Café, Garden Railway).

Bateman, J. & Co. – 1774-c.1900. British. Founded in London, the firm made parts for model steam engines and ships, and from 1879 finished model locomotives. (Train Room, Steam Engine Display).

Beeson, James S. – 1924 onwards. British. James Beeson is acknowledged to be one of the finest model locomotive makers of the century. He began working independently, often subcontracting for the famous names of the day, such as Bassett-Lowke, Leeds Model Company and Walker and Holzapfel. Latterly his production has been exclusively for private clients, principally in gauge 0. (Train Room).

Bets – 1920s. Austrian. A partially completed example of a locomotive by this firm is on display in the Train Room.

Biaggi – 1945 onwards. Italian. Originally marketed as GEM, the firm produced short runs of locomotives in gauges 0 and 1, similar in size and style to pre-Second World War Marklin. (Train Room).

Bing – see Tin Toy Manufacturers. In the field of model locomotives did much work for Bassett-Lowke. (Train Room, Bassett-Lowke Shop).

Bonds – 1920s-1930s. British. One of the principal retailers of Marklin stock in Great Britain, as well as producing model locomotives and other model engineering items of its own. Its shop in Euston Road was world famous. The business is now carried on in Midhurst. (Train Room).

Bowman – Late 1920s-mid 1930s. British. The firm began in business in Norfolk by producing steam engines designed to power Meccano models. Later their range included locomotives, rolling stock and an excellent range of steam-powered boats. (Train Room, Craven Hill Shop).

Brimtoy – 1930s. British. Makers of cheap tin toys principally clockwork toy trains. (Train Room, Craven Hill Shop).

British Flyer – 1920s. American. In 1925 American Flyer tried to market cast-iron engines and lithographed coaches in Britain under the name of 'British Flyer'. However, the line was not a success and was short lived. (Train Room).

British Model & Electrical Company – 1880s-1900. British. Manufactured live-steam brass model locomotives and other scientific models. (Train Room).

Bub, Karl – see Tin Toy Manufacturers (Train Room).

Buco – 1939-50s. Swiss. Appeared during the war-time absence of Marklin – the Hornby trains of Switzerland. (Train Room).

Buddy L – 1930s onwards. American. Part of the Milton Bradley Company, Buddy L toys were principally large scale wheeled toys of rugged pressed steel construction. (Tin Toy Room).

Butcher – 1920s. British. A small firm situated in Watford, specialising in engineer-built locomotives principally for gauge 2. (Train Room).

Carette – see Tin Toy Manufacturers (Train Room, Tin Toy Room, Bassett-Lowke Shop).

Carlisle & Finch – 1894-1916. American. At first produced pocket lamps and batteries and then in 1897 began to produce 2″ electric tramways. Stopped making trains in 1916. (Train Room).

Carson – 1905-13. British. James Carson originally founded the Model Engineer's Cooperative Society in

1904. In 1905, James Carson and Co. took over the society and in 1913 the undertaking was acquired by Bassett-Lowke. The firm specialised in locomotives from gauge 1 to 3½″ gauge. (Train Room)

Chad Valley – see Doll and Soft Toy Manufacturers (Train Room, Craven Hill Toy Shop). The company produced 0 gauge trains which were at best a primitive imitation of Hornby's post-war range.

Clarckson – 1950s-1960s. British. The company's main line was in building large scale live steam locomotives for garden use. They acquired drawings of Jackson of York. Later Reeves of Birmingham took over the business. (Train Room).

Clyde Model Dockyard – 1789-1970. British. Originally manufactured model ships for the Admiralty. Produced model steam engine parts. Much of their production was supplied by Radiguet & Massiot of France, despite claims that everything was 'British made'. (Train Room).

CR – see Rossignol, C.

Darstead – 1960 onwards. Swiss. Founded by Marcel Darphin in order to supply specialist requirements for fine-scale gauge 0 enthusiasts. In addition, Marcel Darphin has produced a more commercial range of 40 cm coaches in the style of pre-war Marklin tinplate. (Train Room).

Doll & Co. – see Tin Toy Manufacturers (Train Room).

Dorfan – 1920-39. American. Founded by Milton and Julius Forcheimer, who were cousins of the founders of the German firm of Kraus. Was the first model railway firm to explore the possibilities of pressure- and die-castings with zinc alloys. Produced electric trains in gauge 0 and standard gauge. (Train Room).

Edobaud – 1931-39. French. Produced a line of giant, electric locomotives and rolling stock in gauge 0 exclusively for Galeries Lafayette. (Train Room).

Elettren – 1945-1980s. Italian. Begun by Armando Ravisini, the company produced trains similar in feel to pre-Second World War Marklin. Later entered into a fruitful collaboration with Fulgurex, in which Elettren supplied most of the gauge 0 rolling-stock production while various Japanese firms produced the locomotives. (Train Room).

Ever Ready – 1950s. British. This battery manufacturing firm produced one battery-operated model train set in 00 scale of the London Underground. (Train Room).

Edward Exley Ltd. – 1924-1980s. British. This company filled a unique role in the world of British model railways by producing a range of scale and semi-scale passenger vehicles. In the late 1930s and early 1950s, Exley's gauge 0 coaches were included in Bassett-Lowke's catalogue. (Train Room).

Farrish, Graham – 1950s-present day. British. This firm began by producing 00 gauge model railways and accessories and later N gauge stock as a subsidiary activity to their main engineering business. (Train Room).

Fleischmann, J. – 1887-present day – see Tin Toy Manufacturers. (Train Room).

Fournereau – 1928-c. 1960. French. This firm was the agent for Bassett-Lowke in France and from 1928 began producing model locomotives, having taken over Marescot's production. Took over various other firms and produced fine models and kits. In 1937 they began the publication of the magazine 'Loco Revue'. (Train Room).

Fulgurex – 1940s-present day. Swiss. One of the few European firms to sponsor the production of high quality, brass, batch-produced scale locomotives in Japan. The accompanying rolling-stock was manufactured by such firms as Wilag, Elettren and Tenshodo. (Train Room).

F.V. (Emile Favre et E.F. Lefevre Successeurs) – 1860-c. 1900. French. Specialised in the manufacture of mechanical tin-plate toys, and was probably the earliest company to provide a range of simple accessories for their trains. (Train Room).

Gaiety – 1950s. British. Produced 00 gauge railway equipment. (Train Room).

Gem – see Biaggi.

Gebauer – 1970s onwards. German. Scale gauge 0 railway equipment. (Train Room).

Gisea – Late 1940s. Italian. Gauge 0 railway equipment. (Train Room).

Gray, Max – 1960s. USA. Importer of Japanese-made American outline railway equipment. (Train Room).

Gunthermann, S. – see Tin Toy Manufacturers. (Train Room).

HAG (H. & A. Gahler) – 1939-early 1950s. Swiss. The firm made metal gauge 0 and HO railway items of Swiss outline. (Train Room).

Hall's Patent – 1880s. British. A little known English toy company whose floor trains appear to have been imported from Germany. (Train Room).

Hermann – Late 1960s onwards. Swiss. Probably the most eminent manufacturers of contemporary Swiss railways in gauge 0. (Train Room).

Hess – see Tin Toy Manufacturers. (Train Room).

Hornby Trains – 1915-1965. British. The first clockwork gauge 0 trains appeared in 1915 but due to the war were not mass-produced until 1920 under the name 'Hornby Trains'. In 1925 the first electric trains appeared and in 1938 a 00 range called Hornby-Dublo. In 1964 Meccano Ltd, the parent firm, was taken over by Lines Bros. and Hornby-Dublo was absorbed into Triang Railways. See also Tin Toy Manufacturers. (Train Room, Meccano Shop).

Hubley – 1894 onwards. American. Founded by John E. Hubley, a factory was built for the manufacture of electric toy train equipment and parts. The firm was taken over in c. 1909 and changed to the manufacture of cast-iron toys, hardware and novelties, including toy trains. (Train Room).

Hubner – 1970s onwards. German. Manufacturer of gauge 0 scale equipment. (Train Room).

Hugar – Mid-1930s-1950s. British. A small English toy-making company noted for its wooden buildings and the introduction of one of the first 2-rail 00 systems. (Train Room).

Ingap – Founded in Padua in 1922, the company produced a wide range of tin toys and ceased business in the 1960s. (Train Room).

Issmayer – see Tin Toy Manufacturers. (Train Room).

Ives – see Tin Toy Manufacturers. (Train Room).

Jackson, H.P. – 1930s-1950s. British. Builder of gauge 1 upwards model railways principally for live-steam running. (Train Room).

JEP – see Tin Toy Manufacturers. (Train Room).

J & M Models – mid-1970s onwards. British. This firm was founded by John Waggott and specialises in high-quality gauge 1 passenger stock of all nations. (Train Room).

Jubb, W.H. – 1915-1920. British. The firm was founded in an attempt to capture the cheaper end of Bassett-Lowke's market which had been so dependent on German manufacturers. Briefly employed Henry Greenly of Bassett-Lowke fame and William Mills who later founded Milbro. However, their production in general was not of a high standard. (Train Room).

Keiser – 1940s onwards. Swiss. Produced 0 gauge electric locomotives. (Train Room).

Kenton Hardware Co. – 1880s. American. Produced cast-iron floor trains and other toys. (Train Room).

Kesselbauer – 1970s. German. Produced a three-car 'Flying Hamburger' set in gauge 0. (Train Room).

Kibri – 1930s. German. Principally a manufacturer of station accessories and buildings. (Train Room).

Kohl, Max. – 1900s. German. Made educational and scientific toys including model locomotives. (Train Room).

Conrad Klein – 1886-1913. German. Manufactured electric toys and equipment, and a small range of trains. (Train Room).

Kraus, J. – 1910-1939. German. Traded under the name of 'Fandor'. Specialised in clockwork and later electric trains in gauges 0 and 1. Set up the sibling firm of Dorfan with relatives in the USA and the founder was forced to flee Nazi persecution in 1938. (Train Room).

KTM – 1960s onwards. Japanese. Participated in the post-Second World War collaboration between Japanese manufacturers of high-quality brass engines and US marketing, producing many fine models. (Train Room).

Leeds Model Company – 1920s-1950s. British. The firm produced a range of gauge 0 locomotives and rolling stock of inconsistent quality. The Japanese firm of Stronlite copied several of their designs. In 1939, the firm produced Bakelite coaches. James Beeson worked for the firm briefly. (Train Room).

Lehmann LGB – 1968 onwards. German. Produces a range of narrow gauge prototypes to gauge 3 scale for gauge 1 track. In 1968 the company was the first to lead the revival of large-gauge scale model trains using mass-production plastic moulding techniques. The company has family links with the famous Lehmann tin toy producing firm. (Train Room).

Lima – 1950s onwards. Italian. Producer of a large range of plastic equipment in HO and gauge 0. (Train Room).

Lines Bros – see Tin Toy Manufacturers.

Lionel – see Tin Toy Manufacturers.

Littledale of Brighton – 1960s onwards. British. Specialises in restoration and painting of vintage and fine scale models. (Train Room).

Lone Star – 1950s. British. The first company to produce a smaller than HO range, approximating to N gauge. (Train Room).

LR (Le Rapide) – 1930s-1954. French. Louis Roussy (a member of the Nestlé family) produced a selection of locomotives for gauge 0. He claimed that they were the 'fastest' model trains ever produced. The company was also one of the first producers of electrically-powered racing car circuits. (Train Room, Tiatsa Room).

Lutz – 1846-1891. German. A toy manufacturer who concentrated mainly on transport toys and dolls house furniture. Lutz goods were marketed by both Bing and Marklin. The latter purchased the firm in 1891. (Train Room).

Maltete et Parent (Later simply *Maltete*) – 1860s-1914. French. Maltete was the successor to Maltete et Parent. A 1902 catalogue shows a wide range of clockwork trains for floor use without rails. (Train Room).

Marescot – 1920s. French. The firm produced the first scale gauge 0 equipment and set new standards in one of Marklin's traditional markets. Was taken over by Fournereau in 1928. (Train Room).

Marklin – see Tin Toy Manufacturers. (Train Room).

Marx – see Tin Toy Manufacturers. (Train Room).

Maskelyne, J.M. – active 1900-1940s. British. One of the pioneers of the model railway hobby both as a modeller and writer. He also issued an extensive series of drawings for modellers and was the editor of 'Model Railway News'. (Train Room).

Meccano – see Hornby, and also Tin Toy Manufacturers. (Train Room, Meccano Shop).

Milbro (Mills Bros. Ltd.) – 1919-1930s. British. The Mills brothers who traded as 'Milbro' were principally noted for their excellent, wooden passenger stock.

Miller, Bernard – c.1930s-1950s. British. Built many of the locomotives for W.S. Norris' famous layout at Byfleet and was an excellent fine-scale model locomotive builder. (Train Room, Flying Scotsman showcase).

Milton Bradley – 1860 to present. USA. Manufactured a very attractive line of wooden toys onto which coloured lithographed paper was stuck. (Train Room).

Moskabel Organisation – 1960s. USSR. Produced a line of very robust metal, gauge 0 locomotives and accessories, not dissimilar to pre-Second World War Lionel. (Train Room).

Newton & Co. – 1870s.-1890s. British. Produced steam-driven brass locomotives and stationary engines of fine quality. (Train Room).

Paya – see Tin Toy Manufacturers. (Train Room).

Plank – see Tin Toy Manufacturers.

Pola Maxi – 1960s-1970s. German. Introduced the first mass-produced moulded plastic 0 gauge equipment in the post-war period. (Train Room).

Precision Models. British. Winteringham, Bassett-Lowke's associated manufacturing arm run by George Winteringham later changed their name to Precision Models. Specialised in model railway items and industrial models. Latterly they were involved in Trix Twin production in England which led to their demise. (Train Room).

Radiguet & Massiot – see Tin Toy Manufacturers. (Train Room).

Rivarossi – 1950s. Italian. Founded by Count Rivarossi in the early 1950s, it became one of Italy's principal manufacturers of scale HO model railway equipment. Later it took over the firm of Pocher. (Train Room).

Rock und Graner – 1813-1904. German. Considered to be the oldest Wurttemberg firm to make enamelled sheet metal toys. 1850-70 were the best years for the firm and trains were added from 1896 until 1904 when the firm was liquidated. (Train Room).

C. Rossignol – see Tin Toy Manufacturers. (Train Room, Tin Toy Room).

Rovex (Triang) – 1940s onwards. British. Rovex models were the scale model department of the Lines Brothers business and were founded just after the Second World War. Their principal line was Triang plastic 00 trains and Scalextric racing car sets. After a series of amalgamations, this part of the firm is today known as 'Hornby Hobbies'. (Train Room).

Rowa – 1960s-1970s. German . Rowa were one of many small independent specialist firms producing HO railway equipment. (Train Room).

Marcel Rossi – active 1930s-1980s. French. Marcel Rossi was a builder of fine-scale passenger stock in gauge 0 and was one of the pioneers in this field in the early 1930s. His models were constructed in card and metal and often included extremely exotic interiors. (Train Room).

Scalecraft 1930s – 1950s. American. Along with Varney and Mantua this firm was one of the initiators of scale modelling in 00 in the US. (Train Room).

Schoenner – see Tin Toy Manufacturers.

Schuco – see Tin Toy Manufacturers.

Stevens & J.E. – see Tin Toy Manufacturers under Stevens & Brown.

Stevens Model Dockyard – 1843-1930. English. Was one of several retailing and manufacturing model concerns that sprung up in England during the nineteenth century. Their range included many brass steam locomotives, boats and stationary engines and a large range of parts for model engineers. (Train Room).

Stronlite – 1930s. Japanese. This firm specialised in gauge 0 electrically-powered equipment based on Japanese and European types. (Train Room).

Tenshodo – 1950s onwards. Japanese. One of the principal post-war Japanese model railway equipment manufacturers. Most of their production was carried out utilising lost-wax brass casting techniques developed in the Far East by model makers. (Train Room).

Trix – Mid-1930s-50s. German/British. Trix was formed in the mid-1930s and produced one of the first HO railway systems and were mainly noted for the Trix Twin railway system. Production was switched to the UK just prior to the Second World War. There were family links with the famous Bing family. (Train Room).

TIN TOYS

Bing – 1863-1932. German. Ignaz and Adolf Bing founded the firm of Gebrüder Bing in 1863 as retailers, and it was not until the early 1880s that they turned to the production of tin toys. Between 1895, the date of incorporation of the manufacturing company and 1914, expansion was rapid. In the years prior to World War 1 the firm employed over 5,000 people. During the 1920s high production levels were maintained, but the world slump, which commenced at the end of this decade, proved disastrous for Bing. A receiver for the company was appointed in 1932, and at some point over the next two years, tin toy production ceased altogether. Soon afterwards Karl Bub took over the company, along with some of the production equipment. (Train Room, Tin Toy Room, Bassett-Lowke Shop, Toy Shop, Café, Nursery, Animal House).

Victor Bonnet et Cie – c.1919-1950s. French. Victor Bonnet et Cie of Paris took over the original Fernand Martin Company soon after World War 1. They continued to produce many of Martin's original toys, using the trade plaque entitled "Les Autos Transports-V.B. & C. à Paris – Made in France". With novelty toys "V.B. et Cie" was merely printed on the box lid. From the late 1940s to the 1950s, they made a series of tin road vehicles using the trademark 'VEBE'. (Fire Engine Showcase).

Brimtoy – 1914-1930s. British. The 'Nelson's Column' trademark was registered on 4 December 1914 and the company produced (possibly in cooperation with Bing) a few tin road vehicles, and later it amalgamated with Wells to form Wells Brimtoy. (Tin Toy Room, Toy Shop).

Karl Bub – 1851-1960s. German. The firm was founded in Nuremburg in 1851. Although little is known of their nineteenth-century production, motor cars and trains were manufactured in the early 1900s. It is known that they produced items in common with Carette and, indeed, continued to list them after Carette's demise in 1917. The precise division of manufacture, as between these firms, is still unresolved. Bub prospered in the 1920s, listing a wide range of motor cars, trains and railway accessories. In the early 1930s, they produced trains previously manufactured by Bing, and examples can be found bearing both Bing and Bub trademarks. Bub's post-1945 history was one of decline. They ceased trading in the 1960s. (Tin Toy Room, Train Room).

Burnett Limited – c.1910 until taken over by Chad Valley. British. Produced some of the best British-made tin toys. The company was originally based in Birmingham but by October 1914 had moved to London. The company was later taken over by Chad Valley. (Bus Display, Toy Shop).

Georges Carette – 1886-1917. German. Georges Carette commenced toy production in Nuremburg in 1886 with the financial backing of the Hopf brewery family. Like Bing, Carette rapidly expanded in the first years of this century and produced a vast range of toys including cars, boats, railways, aircraft, and steam accessories. Georges Carette (although married to a German) retained his French citizenship, and soon after the outbreak of the First World War was forced to return to Paris. The company ceased production in 1917. (Train Room, Tin Toy Room, Bassett-Lowke Shop, Café).

André Citroën – 1923-late 1930s. French. Citroën toys were first produced in 1923 by the parent automobile manufacturer as promotional items. They were almost invariably trademarked by means of a stencilled motif, although occasionally a metal trade-plate was used. Production declined in the late 1930s, being confined to a limited range of models which were still being produced after the Second World War by J.R.D. (Tin Toy Room, Fire Engine Display).

Johann Distler – 1899-1962. German. Founded in the last year of the nineteenth century, the company's best known pre-1914 toys are the range of penny-toy road vehicles, many with either a thistle trademark or the monogram 'J.D.' Later in the 1920s and 1930s, the company produced a wide variety of transport and novelty toys many of which bear no trademark at all. Toys bearing the Distler trademark did appear, however, in the post-war period. (Tin Toy Room, Train Room, Tiatsa Room).

Doll et Cie – 1898-1938. German. Founded by J. Sondheim and Peter Doll, the company in its early years primarily produced stationary steam engines and accessories. Shortly before the First World War, however, when a third partner, Max Bein joined the company, it also turned out several clockwork novelty toys. Doll's production in the 1920s and 1930s was still primarily taken up with steam engines, although it also made trains, a steam car tractor lorry and a traction engine. When the company was taken over by Fleischmann in the late 1930s, the Doll name was retained until the early post-war period. (Tin Toy Room, Stationary Steam Engine Display, Train Room).

Hans Eberl – 1900-c.1914. German. Using the trademark H.E.N., the company was founded in Nuremburg, the centre of the German toy industry. After 1906, a different trademark bearing the words 'Ebo Hui-Hui' and a circle with a boy inside, was adopted. Post-First World War toys by this firm are not known. (Animal House).

H. Fischer & Co. – 1908-late 1930s. German. This Nuremburg firm produced an attractive range of transportation tin toys, with novelty toys being introduced in the 1920s and 1930s. Not all their toys had a trademark, although the distinctive fish trademark is widely found. (Tin Toy Room, Train Room).

J. Fleischmann – 1887-present day. German. Little is known about the firm before the First World War. The model-making department was responsible for producing liners for the publicity department of 'Norddeutsche Lloyd' and a large example of one such model may be seen in the Train Room. Fleischmann were best known in the 1920s and 1930s for their range of toy boats, several of which were to reappear in the 1950s. In 1939 they took over Doll et Cie and commenced model railway production. After the war Fleischmann expanded rapidly and today they are one of the leading manufacturers of model trains. (Train Room).

Gunthermann – 1887-1965. German. Founded by S. Gunthermann in Nuremburg in 1887, the company grew rapidly until by 1901 it was employing 250 people. The founder died in 1890 and his widow married the company manager, Adolf Weigel. His initials are to be found on the early trademarks, along with those of the founder. After Weigel's death in 1919 his initials were removed and the trademark reverted to 'SG'. The company produced a vast range of fine quality tin toys from transportation toys to such well-known novelty toys as 'The Pool Player' and the series of world land-speed record breaking cars. The company was taken over by Siemens in 1965. (Train Room, Tin Toy Room, Brooklands Showcase).

Hausser – 1904-1980s. German. Founded in 1904 and incorporated in 1912 at Ludwigsburg, the firm of Hausser confined itself for several years mainly to the manufacture of wooden toys and composition figures. In the 1930s, the firm expanded rapidly, riding on the success of their tin military vehicles and toy soldiers. Production ceased late in 1942 and recommenced in 1946 with a similar, if limited, range of figures and vehicles, now presented as the Swiss army. Few tin toys were produced after 1957, although Hausser continued to produce, as in their early years, a wide range of wooden toys. The firm closed down in the early 1980s. (Soldier Cabinet, Animal House).

Hess – 1820s-1930s. German. This firm is reputed to have been one of the earliest Nuremburg toymakers when its founder Mathias Hess was making trackless, push-along trains. Later while Marklin and Bing were producing expensive toy trains, such firms as Hess and Issmayer catered to the lower end of the market. Production ended in the early 1930s. (Train Room).

Issmayer – 1861-1930s. German. Issmayer were best known for their small-gauge, finely lithographed trains, marketed by both Bing and Carette. The company was founded in Nuremburg in 1861 by Johann Andreas Issmayer. In the 1880s Issmayer developed sectional tin-plate track using rolled-tin rails and also various gauges of slightly different size. By the turn of the century Issmayer was producing a range of lithographed clockwork railways which were both sophisticated and cheap, often with ingenious mechanisms and movements. However, by the 1920s, the company had lost its earlier drive and it finally went out of business in the early 1930s. (Train Room, Tin Toy Room).

Ives – 1886-1930. American. Founded in 1886 by Edward R. Ives in Plymouth, Connecticut, the company's earliest products were tinplate thermal toys. In 1874, it was Ives, Blakeslee and Company, and moved to Bridgeport, Connecticut. Production increased rapidly, especially in floor trains and clockwork novelty toys. A financial crisis in the late 1890s and a fire in 1900 resulted in new lines being introduced in 1901, notably gauge 0 railway sets. Gauge 1 followed in 1904. Edward R. Ives died in 1918 and the company was taken over and merged into the Lionel Corporation in 1930. (Train Room).

Jep – 1899-1965. French. Jep is believed to have been founded in Paris in 1899 as the Société Industrielle de Ferblanterie (SIF). The change of name to 'Jouets de Paris' (J. de P.) in 1928 coincided with the introduction of an exciting new range of toy cars. Around 1932 the name was changed again to 'Jouets en Paris' (JEP), and it was retained until the company ceased production in 1965. Most Jep toys are clearly trademarked and the firm produced a wide range of railway items and transport toys. (Train Room, Tin Toy Room).

Joustra – 1934-present day. French. The full name of the company is the Société d'Exploitation du Jouet Joustra, 10-12 Rue de Befort, Strasbourg-Neudorf, Bas Rhin. The 1959 25th anniversary catalogue featured many tinplate cars that had been originated by Japanese or German manufacturers, of which the large Cadillac previously manufactured by GAMA, was one

example. (Tin Toy Room, Tiatsa Room, Brooklands Showcase).

Kellerman – 1920s-present day. German. CKO was the trademark of G.G. Kellerman and Company of Nuremburg. They produced tin toys throughout the 1920s and 1930s and became one of the most important of the German tin toy manufacturers in the post-war era. (Animal House, Tiatsa Room).

Kindler and Briel – 1920s-present day. German. This company is based in Boblingen, Germany and used the trademarks 'K. & B.B.' or more often, 'KIBRI'. Today they are prominent plastic kit manufacturers. (Tin Toy Room, Train Room).

Kingsbury – 1895-1940s. American. Before becoming involved with toy production, Harry Thayer Kingsbury started up in business as a result of purchasing component parts for the manufacture of mowers and reapers from the Clipper Machine Works, after a fire at the latter company. In 1895, backed by his grandfather, he went on to purchase the Wilkins Toy Company, producers of toys since 1890. In 1902, Kingsbury patented a distinctive sealed clockwork motor that was to be widely used in successive ranges of toys. Kingsbury retained the Wilkins name for his toy products until 1919 at which time his own name was substituted. During the 1920s and 1930s this company produced the largest range of clockwork automotive toys in the United States. After the Second World War, Kingsbury toys were no longer produced although the Kingsbury Machine Tool Corporation continued in business. (Tin Toy Room, Brooklands Showcase).

Kohnstam – 1875-present day. German. Moses Kohnstam's business, which was established in Furth about 1875, is interesting because, like that of his life-long competitor Eisenmann (trademark 'Einco') it was a pioneer distributor of toys for all but the largest German manufacturers. Kohnstam and Eisenmann acted as commission agents, both collecting toys from a myriad of small German manufacturers, listing them in catalogues, and then offering them for sale on commission throughout Europe. About 1880 they inaugurated the Manchester Toy Week, which was attended by buyers from the north of England and was the forerunner of the Harrogate Toy Fair. Many of the toys sold by Kohnstam bore the trademark 'Moko'. By 1894 the firm had offices in Milan, Brussels and London, but in 1914 the London business was expropriated. After the war, J. Kohnstam Ltd started up in London as a separate business, and in later years the firm was to invent, and register jointly with Lesney Products, the trademark 'Match Box Toys'. J. Kohnstam Ltd was sold to Lesney Products in 1959, and sometime afterwards, Richard Kohnstam, the grandson of the founder, began a new import business known as Richard Kohnstam Limited, using the trademark 'Riko' on many of its lines. In 1969 Richard Kohnstam took over the Beatties chain of model shops, which included the original Bassett-Lowke retail outlets. (Tiatsa Collection).

Lehmann – 1881-present day. German. Ernst Paul Lehmann of Brandenburg commenced toy production in 1881, producing a vast number of ingenious mechanical toys often reflecting topical fashions of the day. When he died in 1934, the company continued under the proprietorship of his cousin, Johannes Richter. After the Second World War, the original Brandenburg factory remained in production in East Germany, while the Richter family, reviving the Lehmann name, commenced toy manufacture in Nuremburg in 1951. (Tin Toy Room, Animal House).

Georg Levy – c.1920-1971. German. Georg Levy was originally a partner in the firm of Hubert Kienburger. He left in 1910, but did not commence actual production on his own account until about 1920. In 1934, due to the rise of Adolf Hitler, he sold his business and emigrated to England. The company then traded under the name 'Nuremburg Tin Toys Factory' until it finally closed down in 1971. The toys were stamped with the word 'Gely' and sometimes the symbol of a double billiard player (which was one of his finest toys). (Tin Toy Room, Craven Hill Toy Shop).

Lineol – 1906-1950s. German. Lineol of Brandenburg was founded by Oskar Wiederholz about 1906. A range of horse-drawn tin vehicles was made in the 1920s, and a range of motorised military vehicles in the 1930s to complement the company's extensive range of model soldiers. Production ceased late in 1942 or early in 1943, recommencing in the post-war years. Little information is available about its subsequent activities as it was located in East Germany. (Soldier Display).

Lines Bros. – 1919-1971. British. The original Lines business was started in 1870 principally to manufacture wooden rocking horses. In 1919, the second generation of Lines brothers formed the company known as Lines Bros. In 1925, the company expanded into the Morden Road factory which became one of the largest toy factories in the world. Products such as Triang dollshouses, pedal cars, Pedigree baby carriages, Minic clockwork toys and Frog and Penguin models and kits were produced by this firm. In 1931, the company registered the name Triang. In 1964, the company took over Meccano Ltd. and in 1971, Lines Bros. went into receivership. (Train Room, Meccano Shop, Craven Hill Toy Shop, Tiatsa Room, Dollshouse Display).

Lionel – 1901-1970. American. Joshua Lionel Cowen started in business with a retail shop in New York in 1901. The first toy he manufactured was an electric tram designed for 73 mm gauge. In 1906 he produced a standard gauge tram and in 1908 a train set. So successful were the sales of these toys that eventually a large factory was established for their production in Irvington, New Jersey. 0 gauge gradually became the dominant product of the company, standard gauge being dropped in 1942. The founder died in 1965 and in 1970, after a troubled period of trading, Model Product Corp, the toy division of General Mills, leased the name and manufacturing rights . (Train Room).

Mangold – German. The Furth-based company of Georg Adam Mangold used the trademark 'Gama' on all their post-Second World War toys. Circumstantial evidence suggests that much of their pre-1939 production was sold to wholesalers like Moses Kohnstam of Furth. (Tiatsa Collection).

Marklin – 1859-present day. German. The Marklin company (initially W. Marklin Company) was founded by Theodor Friedrich Wilhelm Marklin and his wife Caroline in Goppingen in 1859. Their earliest toys were dolls' cooking utensils. When the founder died in 1886 Mrs. Marklin took sole charge of the firm, until in 1888 her two sons, Eugen and Karl, succeeded to it, renaming it Gebruder Marklin. Caroline Marklin died in 1893, a year after the firm's name had been expanded to Gebruder Marklin and Company with the addition of E. Fritz as a joint proprietor. Tin boats, trains and horse-drawn vehicles were all produced in the 1890s, the firm having absorbed the early tin toy maker Lutz at about that time, and the number of employees reached 600 in 1914. In 1907 the company's name was changed to Gebruder Marklin Cie. Eugen Marklin remained on the board of directors until 1935. His son, Fritz Eugen Marklin, who was the last of the Marklin family within the management company, died in 1961. The company still produces a wide range of quality toys, and maintains its record for being the oldest manufacturer of model trains in the world. (Train Room, Tin Toy Room, Bassett-Lowke Shop, Nursery, Doll Room).

F. Martin – 1878-1920s. French. The company, founded in Paris by Fernand Martin, was one of the most productive of the early novelty-toy manufacturers, turning out as many as 800,000 mechanical toys a year. The founder died in 1919 and a few years later the company was taken over by Victor Bonnet et Cie. (Tin Toy Room).

Marx – 1920s-present day. American. Louis Marx is a famous American toy manufacturer who was noted for his tin novelty toys in the 1920s and 1930s. The company also had an English subsidiary based in Dudley and later South Wales, using the same name and trademark. The English company was registered on 12 September 1932. (Train Room).

Meccano Ltd – 1908-1964. British. Meccano planes and cars, together with Hornby boats and trains, were all produced by Meccano Limited. This company was first registered in 1908 as a successor to Frank Hornby's original firm, which had traded since 1901 as Frank Hornby and latterly as Elliott & Hornby. The first 0 gauge clockwork train was put on the market in 1920, and the first electric train in 1925. Meccano cars and planes, Hornby boats and Dinky Toys followed in the 1930s.

The company also produced the long-running "Meccano Magazine" for devotees of the various lines. In 1964 the original company, whose founder had died in 1936, was taken over by Lines brothers. Almost all Meccano's products are clearly trademarked. Meccano also had factories in Bobigny, France and up to 1928 in New Jersey, USA. (Meccano Shop).

J. Ph. Meier – 1894-1920s. German. The 'Dog Cart' trademark was registered in 1894 by J. Ph. Meier, a tin toy manufacturer in Nuremburg best known for his wide range of penny toys. Only a few larger toys have been attributed to this company. Moses Kohnstam continued to market their penny toys during the 1920s. (Penny Toy Display).

Mettoy Co. Limited – 1933-present day. British. A company founded by Henry Ullmann, formerly a proprietor of Tipp and Company, after his enforced emigration from Germany in 1933. In the 1930s and early post-war years, the firm made a number of tinplate toys, usually trademarked 'Mettoy'. In 1979 the company ceased business in Northampton and was latterly transferred under new ownership to South Wales. Today this company is well-known as the manufacturer of diecast 'Corgi Toys'. (Tin Toy Room, Brooklands Showcase, Tiatsa Room).

Muller and Kadeder – active 1900-1914. German. An obscure Nuremburg company, most active between 1900 and 1912, it produced a number of most attractive carousels, zeppelins, aircraft and novelty toys, none of which have trademarks. (Tin Toy Room).

Orobr – c. 1900-1930. German. The full name of the company was 'Oro' Werke Neil, Blechschmidt and Muller of Brandenburg. The company made a variety of cheap lithographed tin toys before the First World War and again in the 1920s. (Tin Toy Room).

Paya – c. 1905-present day. Spanish. Founded in the early years of this century by Raimundo Paya in Ibi, near Alicante, Spain, the firm made simple toys and floor trains, and beginning in the 1920s, 0 gauge train sets. Tin toys are still being produced from a second factory in Alicante, and are usually trademarked 'Paya'. (Train Room, Tin Toy Room).

Ernst Plank – 1866-1930s. German. The Nuremburg company of Ernst Plank, founded in 1866, was renowned for its brass engines and magic lanterns. Tin toy steam accessories, cars, boats, trains followed about the turn of the century. Tin toy production ceased in the 1930s when the firm was taken over by Schuller Brothers who specialised in home film equipment. (Train Room, Tin Toy Room).

Radiguet – 1872-1902. French. Founded in Paris by M. Radiguet, who later (in 1899) went into partnership with Massiot. The company is most famous for its superb brass engines and steam boats, many of which were exported as complete models or parts. There is no evidence of toy production after 1902, and their toys were not normally trademarked. (Train Room, Tin Toy Room).

C. Rossignol – 1868-1962. French. Charles Rossignol founded the company that was to bear his name in Paris about 1868, producing floor trains and afterwards a series of motor cars and 0 and 1 gauge trains. In the 1920s, they introduced a range of Paris buses which was to continue until the company went out of business in 1962. The trademark monogram 'CR', appears in various forms on almost all Rossignol toys. (Train Room, Tin Toy Room).

Jean Schoenner – 1875-1906. German. Jean Schoenner founded his company in 1875 in Nuremburg. The factory, which had to be completely re-equipped after a fire in 1891, limited its production in its early years to steam engines and magic lanterns, but widened its scope about the turn of the century to take in boats and fire engines, the majority of them powered by steam. There is no evidence of Schoenner's having continued production after about 1906, although it seems that some of the firm's tooling was taken over by J. Falk. (Train Room).

Schuco – 1912-present day. German. Founded by Herr Schreyer and Heinrich Muller, the company traded under the name of Schreyer and Company with the trademark 'Schuco'. It made a range of ingenious mechanical toys in the 1930s and again in the post-war years. (Tin Toy Room, Toy Shop, Animal House).

Stevens and Brown Manufacturing Company – 1869-1880. American. This company was founded in Cromwell, Connecticut, and was an amalgamation of the tin toy manufacturing company of George Brown and J. and E. Steven's firm who produced a successful line of cast-iron toys and banks. This company continued trading until 1880, during which time they formed a wholesale distribution house in New York City known as the 'American Toy Company'. (Doll Display).

Sutcliffe – 1885-present day. British. The company was founded by J.W. Sutcliffe in Horsforth, Leeds. It produced its first toy boats in 1920. The company is now run by the son of the founder and still produces simple tinplate boats. (Tin Toy Shop).

Tipp and Company – 1912-1971. German. Founded by Miss Tipp and Mr. Carstens, Miss Tipp was succeeded in the first year by Philip Ullmann, and by 1919 he was the sole proprietor. The company prospered over the next decade and until 1933, when Ullmann was forced to emigrate to England, the firm being taken over by the German Government and placed under the management of a former Bing director. Production increased in the 1930s with a growing emphasis upon toys based on military equipment. Toy production ceased altogether in 1942. After the war in October 1948, the company was returned to Ullmann. A wide range of tin toys was made in the 1950s and 1960s, but in 1971 the company closed down. (Tin Toy Room).

Wells Brimtoy Limited – 1923-1960s? British. This London company made a wide variety of tinplate road vehicles in the 1920s and 1930s and again in the post-war years. (Tin Toy Room, Craven Hill Toy Shop, Brooklands Showcase).

Whiteley Tansley and Company Limited – 1916-1930s. British. 'Whitanco' was the trademark of this company which was founded in Liverpool in 1916. A number of attractive tin road vehicles were made by this small company. (Tin Toy Room, Craven Hill Toy Shop).

JAPANESE TOYS

After the Second World War, Japan took over as the world's largest manufacturer of tinplate toys, a position previously enjoyed by Germany. The museum has many examples of Japanese tinplate which was often motorised by means of clockwork motors or, latterly, batteries. Many of the Japanese tinplate cars were based on American models, while a good selection of novelty toys and in particular novelty teddy bears may be seen in the Animal House. Unfortunately, little is known at present of the individual company histories and what follows is a list of the major manufacturers on view in the museum together with the year of their foundation, if available:

> Alps – 1948
> Asahi – 1950
> Bandai – 1950
> Haji – 1951
> MT (K.K. Masutoku Toy Factory) – 1924
> Rabbit Trademark (Usagiya) – 1950
> SH (Horikawa Toys) – 1959
> Taiyo – 1959
> TN (Nomura Toys Ltd) – 1923
> TPS (Toplay Ltd) – 1956

DIE-CAST TRANSPORT TOYS AND MODELS

Budgie Toys.– 1960s and 1970s. British. Budgie Toys was a new name for a range which had been produced by Morestone since the 1950s. It was more successful and by the mid-1960s there were some 60 different models. Morestone were the first of the manufacturers to introduce a die-cast character car, namely "Noddy and His Car" in the late 1960s. (Tiatsa Room).

Charbens – 1930s-1960s. British. This company formed by Charles Benson produced some of the first British die-casts in emulation of the American-made Tootsietoys, as well as a range of lead figures such as the Mickey Mouse series. (Craven Hill Toy Shop).

Corgi Toys – 1955-1983. British. Corgi Toys were launched at the British Industries Fair early in 1955 and were part of the Mettoy Company. They were introduced to compete with Dinky Toys and were successful in this, due to their constant introduction of new gimmicks such as "The First With Windows". Later the firm produced what could arguably be called the most successful die-cast ever – the James Bond Aston Martin. (Tiatsa Room).

Dinky Toys – 1933-1979. British. Dinky Toys were part of the famous Meccano Empire (see Tin Toy Manufacturers) and were introduced in direct response to the American Tootsietoy range. Dinky Toys were the first British toy cars produced using advanced die-casting techniques. By the mid-1930s, Dinky Toys were undisputed market leaders and the range soon included ships, aeroplanes, military vehicles, commercial transport, dollshouse furniture, garden and farm equipment and even sheep. By the late 1950s, Dinky had begun to lose its pre-eminence in the field due to such revivals as Corgi, Tekno and Solido. (Meccano Shop, Tiatsa Room).

Lesney – 1947-present day. British. The firm was initially founded to manufacture commercial die-casting for other companies and then in 1949 Lesney began to make its own toys as a side-line. At first these were large and inconsistent in scale. In 1953, Lesney re-issued a large model of the State Processional Coach originally made in 1950 and introduced a smaller one which was a best-seller. This success led to the introduction of the first three Matchbox toys in the same year. By 1960, Lesney was the market leader in its size range and remained so until c.1970. Windows and opening parts had begun to appear in 1960. 1956 saw the launch of Lesney's famous Models of Yesteryear appealing both to adult and child, and these have remained the biggest seller in their field. (Tiatsa Room).

Solido – 1938-present day. French. Introduced as a rival to French Dinky, Solido has remained the most successful and prolific manufacturer of French die-cast transport vehicles. (Tiatsa Room).

Spot-on – 1959-68. British. Spot-on was the trade name for a range of die-cast vehicles launched by Tri-ang. However, when the company acquired Meccano in 1964, the Spot-on range was gradually abandoned in favour of Dinky Toys. Spot-on was unique in that every model in the range was made to a constant 1/42nd scale. (Tiatsa Room).

Tootsietoys – 1910-1930s. American. Tootsietoys were a range launched by the Dowst company and apparently the name came from the nickname given to Dowst's daughter. Tootsietoys produced the first die-cast miniature cars and not surprisingly the company's first recognisable model was of the famous Model 'T' Ford. By the late 1920s, Tootsietoys was established as the world's largest manufacturer of die-cast toys. In the late 1930s Tootsietoys was renamed "Playtoys".

Western Models – 1974-present day. British. Western manufactures both white metal kits and completed models. As the techniques of casting white metal have improved, Western has been able to produce larger and more finely detailed vehicles. (Tiatsa Room).

In addition the museum also has die-cast toys by the following manufacturers:

British	French	German
Brooklyn	Champion	Gama
DG Models	Eligor	Marklin
Somerville	Norev	Prameta
Victory		Schuco
		Wiking
		Zeiss

Indian	Israeli	Italian
Maxwell	Gamda	Brunon
Milton		Burago
Nikitoy		Mebetoy
		Mercury
		Politoy
		Rio

Japanese	Soviet	Spanish
Yonezawa	Collection of	Paya
	military diecasts	

Swedish	New Zealand
Tekno	Fun Ho!

These are all on view in the Tiatsa Room.

FLATS, SEMI-SOLIDS AND SOLID FIGURES

Britain's Ltd, William – London, England. 1884 to present. Manufacturers of a vast range of metal figures, mainly soldiers, and other mechanical toys such as automatic walking race. Also toys using a special fly-wheel. Use of hollow casting using an alloy instead of solid lead. By 1902, 104 different regiments were being made. (Soldier Display, Nursery, Animal House, Craven Hill Toy Shop).

Haffner, Johann – Firth, Germany. Founded 1838. Made a range of the 1870 Franco-German war figures. Made flats, semi-flats and solids. Later taken over by Albrecht Stadtler. (Soldier Displays).

Heinrich – 1890-1920. German. This firm first registered the G.H. trademark in 1895. They exported a large range of metal toy soldiers to Great Britain and much of their production was until recently considered to be the work of Heyde. (Soldier Displays).

Heinrichson – Nuremburg, Germany. 1839-1945. Produced flats of the Prussian Guards, Bavarian Infantry and French lancers. In 1848 introduced the 30 mm Heinrichson, or Nuremburg scale, which was widely adopted as a standard. Later members of the family widened the range considerably. (Soldier Displays).

Heyde, Georg – Dresden, Germany. c. 1870-c. 1940. Manufacturer of semi-solids and solids. Exported large numbers of soldiers, including Romans and Greeks, North American Indians and scenes from the American War of Independence. (Soldier Displays).

Lucotte – c. 1780s-1820s. French. The Lucotte factory was in production at the time of the storming of the Bastille and made figures connected with that event.

Their figures bear the trademark L.C. In the early nineteenth century the firm was absorbed by C.B.G. Mignot. (Soldier Displays).

Mignot – Paris, France. Founded 1825. Most famous of the French soldier manufacturers, producing solids, flats and some hollow figures. Several amalgamations of the firm with others took place. The main items produced were figures from the French armies. (Soldier Displays).

CONSTRUCTIONAL TOYS

Bayko – 1930s. British. "Bayko" was the trade name used by the Plympton Engineering Company of Liverpool who manufactured a range of unique building assembly outfits using steel rods and plastic sections. (Meccano and Craven Hill Toy Shops).

Bing – (see Tin Toy Manufacturers) – The company also produced a range of children's building blocks in addition to its enormous range of tinplate toys. (Craven Hill Toy Shop).

Chad Valley – 1823. British. The firm was founded by Anthony Bunn Johnson and the early products were simply printed stationery. In 1897 a toy factory was opened by the Chad stream at Harborne on the outskirts of Birmingham and the Chad Valley trade mark was first used. Card construction sets were introduced and included houses, forts, villas and schools. In the 1930s, craft sets were a major feature and a new construction toy of the liner Queen Mary was produced. In 1947 the company was marketing the "Ubilda" Car previously produced by Burnett whom they had taken over. (Craven Hill Toy Shop).

Erector – see Structo.

Kliptiko – 1920s. British. This was the trade name for a constructional system using various tinplate parts which clipped together and enabled the child to make cranes, towers or bridges. (Craven Hill Toy Shop).

Lott's – 1918-1960s. British. The company advertised itself as makers of "Stone Bricks" and "Tudor Blocks" which were at first made from ground-down Italian marble. The company later took over the famous Richter plant manufacturing similar bricks and later the bricks were cut to more advanced shapes making possible the construction of cathedrals, etc. To add extra variety various different coloured bricks were also introduced. (Nursery, Craven Hill Toy Shop).

Marklin – Constructor Sets – 1930s. German. (See also Tin Toy Manufacturers). In addition to being one of the largest manufacturers of tin toys, Marklin also turned to the manufacture of constructional toys in the 1920s. During this time Meccano and Marklin were involved in various commercial arrangements. (Craven Hill Toy Shop).

Meccano – 1901-1975. British. (See also Tin Toy Manufacturers). Meccano is undoubtedly the most famous construction system ever invented with the first patent being issued in 1901. The system, invented by Frank Hornby, consisted of metal strips half an inch wide with equal holes at half-inch intervals. The sizes were never altered and therefore father and son could share their sets with ease. The company was originally called Elliott & Hornby, but in 1908 the name was changed to Meccano Ltd. In 1912, Meccano France was set up. In 1922, a factory was opened in the United States. In 1979, the company went into liquidation and was taken over by Airfix. In 1981, Airfix went into liquidation. Currently the rights to produce Meccano are owned by Mark Rebibo and the parts are produced in Calais. (Meccano Shop).

Primus Engineering – 1920s. British. Produced construction sets including a locomotive and carriages from a 100-part set. Encountered legal problems with Meccano. (Train Room).

Richter – 1879-1920s. German. The firm is thought to have been founded in the middle ages, although the first sign was registered in 1879 and their building blocks were patented in 1880. The firm advertised that they supplied bricks to the Emperor of Austria and "the little princes and princesses of the Royal and Imperial Nurseries of Europe". Real stone was used and a large set could weigh up to half a hundredweight. Altogether 328 different shapes and sizes of brick were made enabling the aspiring architect to construct castles, towers, bridges, streets and villages. (Nursery).

Structo – 1908-1975. American. Founded by Louis and Edward Strohacker and C.C. Thompson in order to make "Erector Construction Kits". in 1911, Structo was sued by Meccano for patent infringement and, alhough Structo won the case, Meccano later acquired the patents and merged with A.C. Gilbert in order to sell Erector Sets in the U.S. Structo sold both construction kits and ready-built automotive toys. (Tin Toy Room, Craven Hill Toy Shop).

Ubilda – 1920s. British. This range of toys was part of the Burnett company (later taken over by Chad Valley) and included a car, an aeroplane, a locomotive, a fire engine, and Tower Bridge made from tinplate. (Tin Toy Room).

The museum also has examples of constructional toys which were produced during the 1930s and 1940s by Apex, Dux, JEP and Wenebrik. (Craven Hill Toy Shop).

The museum also has examples of plastic kit toys by the following manufacturers:

Airfix	Matchbox
Frog	Skybird
Hubley	Tamiya
Keelcraft	Warnfield

These may be seen in the Craven Hill Toy Shop and the Special Exhibition Room.

PAPER CUT-OUTS AND BOARD GAMES

Benjamin Pollock Ltd – 1876-present day. British. In 1876, Benjamin Pollock, then aged 20, took over the shop and stock of John Redington a publisher of plays. He went on to publish many more plays as well as the very attractive paper theatres that accompanied them. (Nursery).

Raphael Tuck – 1865-present day. British. Raphael Tuck left Germany in 1865 and came to London where he opened a framing shop. By 1881, the firm was changed to Raphael Tuck & Sons and was producing books, wall charts, cards, paper novelties, marionettes, paper dolls and scraps. A Royal Warrant of Appointment to Queen Victoria was granted in 1893 and after her death, the names of succeeding monarchs also appeared. (Soldier Cabinet).

BOARD GAMES

The museum has a collection of various board games on display mainly in the Nursery and Craven Hill Toy Shop and including examples by the following manufacturers:

    Ideal – American

    Matthews, Spears, Victory, Waddington, Edward Wallis – English.

DOLLS AND SOFT TOYS

Alexander Doll Co – Founded 1923. Produced rag-doll characters from Dickens and later widened the range as well as using plastics and vinyl. (Doll Room).

Armand Marseille (A & M) – Koppelsdorf, Thuringia, Germany. 1890-1925. The firm began with the production of bisque heads in 1890 and these were made for many other firms. Although a prolific manufacturer, high quality was maintained. (Doll Room).

Bru (Bru Jnr & Cie) – French. 1866-1899. Founded by Leon Casimir Bru. The dolls have pink or white kid bodies and limbs of porcelain or wood. The heads were of porcelain, rubber or hardened paste. Today these dolls are highly sought after both for their rarity and their charm of expression. (Doll Room).

Chad Valley – Birmingham, England. Founded 1823. Chad Valley factory opened in 1897. In 1913 were making construction sets. (See also 'Constructional Toys'). Mascots and animals made from 1920. In 1927, 'Bambina' dolls and Mabel Lucie Attwell figures were issued. Bonzo, the 'Famous Study Dog' was issued in 1929. In 1933-34 calico was used instead of plush. The firm still produces soft toys today. (Doll Room).

Deans and Son, Deans Rag Book Company – Rye, England. Founded 1903 making rag books for children and is still in production today. Printed rag dolls were issued pre the First World War until World War Two. Soft toys were produced before the First World War. The company is now the sole agent for the Merrythought company. (Animal House, Nursery).

Gebrüder Heubach – Lichte, Thuringia, Germany. Founded 1820. One of the earlier German doll companies, noted for their character dolls and all-bisque dolls. Usually marked with the rising sun of 'Heubach'. (Doll Room).

Ideal Novelty & Toy Company – Brooklyn, New York. Founded by Morris Michton in 1907 and made the first teddy bears on the market. (Nursery).

Jumeau – Paris, France. Founded 1842 by Pierre François Jumeau. Taken over in 1875 by Emile Jumeau, the younger son. Probably one of the most famous names among doll manufacturers. A large number of outworkers were used to make the beautiful clothes which accurately copied the fashions of the day. The two main types were the bebes and the parisiennes. The bodies were usually leather and the limbs of leather, wood or porcelain. In 1889 the firm claimed to employ 1,000 workers and to be selling 300,000 dolls per week. (Doll Room).

Kämmer & Reinhardt (K*R) – Waltershausen, Germany. Founded c.1886. In 1902 took over the Heinrich Hanwerck factory. Best known for their wide range of character dolls. Between 1902 and 1927 the heads for the dolls were made by a variety of other manufacturers. In 1927 the company took over the production of Simon & Halbig heads. By 1932, K*R was the leading doll company in Waltershausen. (Doll Room).

Kling, C.F. & Co – Ohrduf, Thuringia, Germany. 1836-1925. Manufacturer of jointed all-porcelain dolls known as Parians. These dolls usually had finely painted features and blond hair. (Doll Room).

Lenci – Founded in 1920. Lenci was the trade name of Enrico Scavini of Turin. These attractive predominantly felt dolls were apparently designed by Italian artists and the faces were moulded felt, painted by hand. Over 100 different models were in production by 1921. Marked on the foot with labels and/or button. (Doll Room).

Merrythought Toys – Dale End, Ironbridge, Shropshire. Founded 1930 and in production ever since making soft toys in fur and felt. (Doll Room).

Pedigree Dolls and Toys Ltd – Canterbury, England. Founded in 1938, this was the first firm to make high-quality composition dolls. Best known today for the 'Sindy Doll' first produced in 1962. (Doll Room).

Franz Schmidt – Gegenthal, Germany. Founded c.1890. Made dolls' bodies and parts. Had close links with Simon & Halbig. (Doll Room).

A. Schoenhut & Co. – Philadelphia, USA. 1872-1925. The most famous product of this toy company was the wooden, jointed 'Humpty Dumpty Circus' first produced in 1903. (Animal House).

Simon & Halbig – Grafenhain, Thuringia, Germany. Made a great variety of dolls' heads in Parian and papier mâché. Apart from the all-bisque dolls, the company did not make bodies and these were bought in. Made heads for various German and French firms such as Kämmer & Reinhardt and Jumeau. (Doll Room).

Steiff – Giengen an der Brenz, Germany. Registered in 1893 under the names of Margarete Steiff and Fritz Steiff. Characteristic button trade mark used from 1905. 1906 became an incorporated company. By 1907 the firm was producing 974,000 teddy bears per annum and by 1909 employed nearly 3,000 workers producing a vast range of animal toys as well as felt-faced dolls. The firm is still in production today and is one of the largest and most famous manufacturers of soft toys. (Nursery).

Wellings, Nora – Wellington, Shropshire, England. 1926-59. Between these years, Nora Wellings worked at the Victoria Toy Works producing a very charming range of felt, plush, velvet and fur cloth toys. (Doll Room).

OTHER TOY MUSEUMS IN LONDON

The Museum of Childhood
Bethnal Green, Cambridge Heath Road,
London E2 9PA.

Pollocks Toy Museum
1 Scala Street, London W1.

METTOY PLAYTHINGS

ALL METAL
CLOCKWORK

No. 2007

MONOPLANE, with detachable wing.
MONOPLAN, avec aile détachable.
MONOPLANO, con ala desmontable.

11 x 13½ x 3¼ inches.   4½ ozs.
280 x 345 x 85 mm.   130 gms.

No. 2009

MONOPLANE, with detachable wing.
MONOPLAN, avec aile détachable.
MONOPLANO, con ala desmontable.

13 x 14½ x 3½ inches.   6½ ozs.
330 x 370 x 90 mm.   185 gms.

No. 2011

MONOPLANE, with detachable w
MONOPLAN, avec aile détachable
MONOPLANO, con ala desmontab

11½ x 17 x 3½ inches.   5½ oz
290 x 430 x 90 mm.   155 gm

This museum is primarily concerned with the development of the mechanical toy and it is interesting to note how toy making followed political and economic events. The following pages show British tin toy production of the immediate post-war period.

Mettoy was a business founded by refugees from pre-war Germany and so a great tradition of toy making was passed on to the host nation.

With the decline of tin toy making in Europe, Japan later became predominant.

Toys of the immediate post-war period are particularly evocative as they came after a period when virtually no toys were manufactured for British children. Perhaps this is why this museum exists!

2

"METTOY" BRITISH MADE

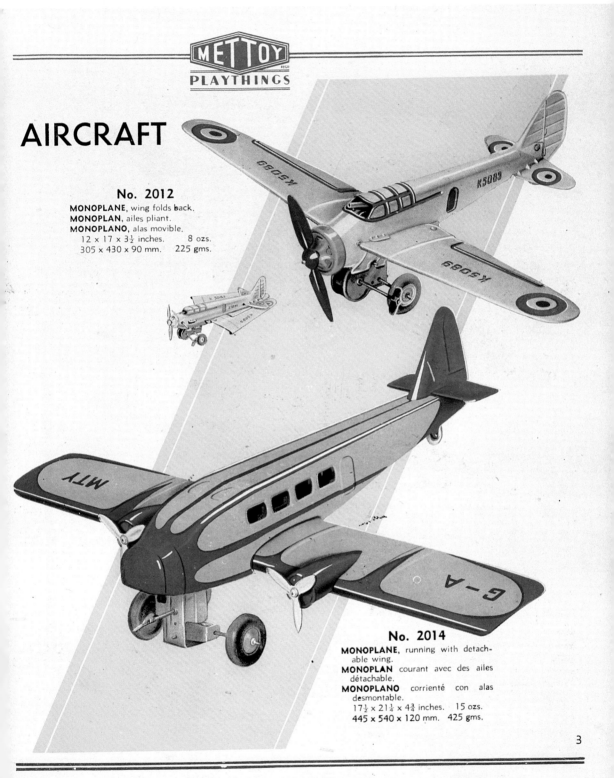

MET TOY
PLAYTHINGS

AIRCRAFT

No. 2012
MONOPLANE, wing folds back.
MONOPLAN, ailes pliant.
MONOPLANO, alas movible.
 12 x 17 x 3½ inches.   8 ozs.
 305 x 430 x 90 mm.   225 gms.

No. 2014
MONOPLANE, running with detachable wing.
MONOPLAN courant avec des ailes détachable.
MONOPLANO corrienté con alas desmontable.
 17½ x 21¼ x 4¾ inches.   15 ozs.
 445 x 540 x 120 mm.   425 gms.

3

MODERN MECHANICAL TOYS

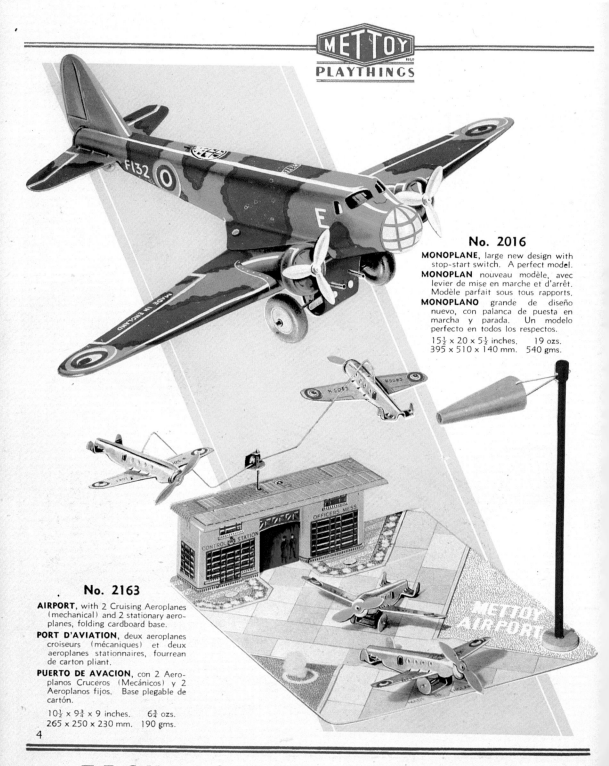

No. 2016

MONOPLANE, large new design with stop-start switch. A perfect model.

MONOPLAN nouveau modèle, avec levier de mise en marche et d'arrêt. Modèle parfait sous tous rapports.

MONOPLANO grande de diseño nuevo, con palanca de puesta en marcha y parada. Un modelo perfecto en todos los respectos.

$15\frac{1}{2} \times 20 \times 5\frac{1}{2}$ inches.   19 ozs.
395 x 510 x 140 mm.   540 gms.

No. 2163

AIRPORT, with 2 Cruising Aeroplanes (mechanical) and 2 stationary aeroplanes, folding cardboard base.

PORT D'AVIATION, deux aeroplanes croiseurs (mécaniques) et deux aeroplanes stationnaires, fourrean de carton pliant.

PUERTO DE AVACION, con 2 Aeroplanos Cruceros (Mecánicos) y 2 Aeroplanos fijos. Base plegable de cartón.

$10\frac{1}{2} \times 9\frac{3}{4} \times 9$ inches. $6\frac{3}{4}$ ozs.
265 x 250 x 230 mm.   190 gms.

4

TECHNICALLY DESIGNED

MECHANICAL AUTOMOBILES

No. 3023
ROADSTER.
CABRIOLET.
CABRIOLE.
8 x 4 x 2¾ inches.   5 ozs.
205 x 100 x 70 mm.   140 gms.

No. 3035
STAFF CAR.
AUTO LIMOUSINE MILITAIRE.
AUTOMOVIL LIMUSINA MILITAR.
9 x 4 x 3¼ inches.   6¾ ozs.
230 x 100 x 85 mm.   190 gms.

No. 3035T
CAR AND TRAILER (Y.M.C.A. TEA CAR).
AUTO et remorque.
AUTOMOVIL y caravano.
17¾ x 4 x 3¾ inches.   12½ ozs.
450 x 100 x 95 mm.   355 gms.

5

TRUE-TO-SCALE MODELS

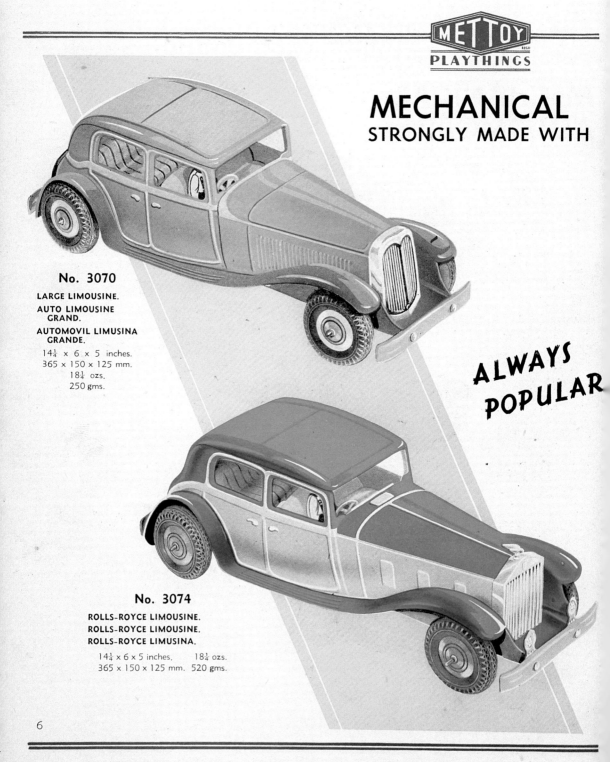

MECHANICAL
STRONGLY MADE WITH

No. 3070

LARGE LIMOUSINE.
AUTO LIMOUSINE GRAND.
AUTOMOVIL LIMUSINA GRANDE.

14¼ x 6 x 5 inches.
365 x 150 x 125 mm.
18¼ ozs.
250 gms.

ALWAYS POPULAR

No. 3074

ROLLS-ROYCE LIMOUSINE.
ROLLS-ROYCE LIMOUSINE.
ROLLS-ROYCE LIMUSINA.

14¼ x 6 x 5 inches. 18¼ ozs.
365 x 150 x 125 mm. 520 gms.

6

ATTRACTIVE COLOURINGS

METTOY PLAYTHINGS

AUTOMOBILES
RELIABLE MECHANISM

WITH THE CHILDREN!

No. 3088

RACING CAR, long bonnet, high powered, with adjustable front wheels.

PUISSANTE AUTO DE COURSE, à long capot, avec roues de devant adjustables.

AUTOMOVIL DE CARRERAS de gran potencia, con ruedas delanteras ajustables.

$12\frac{3}{4} \times 4\frac{3}{4} \times 4$ inches. $9\frac{1}{2}$ ozs.
$320 \times 120 \times 100$ mm.   270 gms.

No. 3104

FIRE ENGINE with large double ladder.
MACHINE CONTRE INCENDIE avec grande échelle double.
MAQUINA CONTRA INCENDIOS y escalera grandè doble.

$11\frac{3}{4} \times 4\frac{1}{2} \times 4\frac{1}{2}$ inches. $8\frac{3}{4}$ ozs.
$300 \times 115 \times 115$ m.m.   250 gms.

7

REALISTIC DESIGNS

MECHANICAL
COMMERCIAL

No. 3114

PETROL LORRY.
CAMION A ESSENCE.
CAMION DE GASOLINA.

8 x 4 x 3¼ inches.   6¼ ozs.
205 x 100 x 85 mm.   175 gms.

No. 3116

TIP LORRY.
CAMION.
CAMION.

7¾ x 3¼ x 3¼ inches.   5 ozs.
195 x 85 x 85 mm.   140 gms.

No. 3110
LARGE FIRE ENGINE with
elaborate mechanical fitment
for extending ladder on
movable turntable.
**GRANDE MACHINE CONTRE
INCENDIE,** avec méchanisme
élaboré contrôlant une
échelle à coulisse montée sur
plaque tournante.
**MAQUINA CONTRA INCEN-
DIOS GRANDE** con accesorio
mecánico elaborado que actua
una escala corrediza montada
sobre una placa giratoria.

15¼ x 6 x 7 inches.   22½ ozs.
390 x 150 x 180 mm.   640 gms.

8

ACTION !

VEHICLES

No. 3116B

REMOVAL VAN (cardboard container).

VOITURE DE DEMENAGEMENT (contenant de carton).

CONDUCTORA, DE MUEBLES (contenedor de cartón).

$7\frac{1}{2}$ x 4 x $3\frac{3}{4}$ inches. $4\frac{1}{4}$ ozs.
190 x 100 x 95 mm.   120 gms.

No. 3118

6 WHEELER LORRY.
CAMION AVEC 6 ROUES.
CAMION CON 6 RUEDAS.

9 x 4 x $3\frac{1}{4}$ inches. $5\frac{1}{4}$ ozs.
230 x 100 x 85 mm.   150 gms.

No. 3124

6 WHEEL TIPPER LORRY with special tipping jack and rear opening.

CAMION-AUTO A RENVERSEMENT, A 6 ROUES, avec arrière-porte et appareil basculant spécial.

CAMION BASCULADOR CON 6 RUEDAS, dispositivo de volteo especial y puerta trasera.

$12\frac{1}{2}$ x $4\frac{1}{2}$ x $3\frac{1}{2}$ inches. $11\frac{1}{4}$ ozs.
320 x 115 x 90 mm.   320 gms.

9

REALISM!

PLAYTHINGS

No. 3125

LARGE TIP LORRY.
CAMION A DECHARGE GRAND.
CAMION VOLCADOR GRANDE.

$11\frac{1}{4}$ x $4\frac{1}{2}$ x 4 inches. $8\frac{3}{4}$ ozs.
285 x 115 x 100 mm.   250 gms.

No. 3123/1

Large **BOX TRANSPORT VAN,** 6
wheeled, with single door at rear.
Grande **VOITURE DE DEMENAGE-
MENT** avec porte unique a l'arriere.
CAMION grande, **TRANSPORTADOR
DE MUEBLES,** con 6 ruedas y una
sola puerta trasera.

10 x $4\frac{1}{4}$ x 4 inches.   10 ozs.
255 x 105 x 100 mm.   280 gms.

No. 3123/2

AMBULANCE.
L'AMBULANCE.
LA AMBULANCIA.

10 x $4\frac{1}{4}$ x 4 inches.   10 ozs.
255 x 105 x 100 mm.   280 gms.

10

"METTOY" BRITISH MADE

METTOY PLAYTHINGS

No. 3126A

SIX WHEEL LORRY with special detachable aeroplane.

CAMION-AUTO A 6 ROUES, avec aéroplane spécial détachable.

CAMION CON 6 RUEDAS, llevando un avión especial que puede separarse del mismo.

16 x 4½ x 4½ inches.   14½ ozs.
405 x 115 x 115 mm.   410 gms.

No. 3128

Modern **EIGHT WHEEL LORRY** with detachable truck fitted with stationary device.

CAMION-AUTO moderne, comprenant une voiturette détachable, avec déclanchement fixe.

CAMION MODERNO con carro de remolque separable provisto de dispositivo de apoyo para mantenerlo horizontal cuando se desengancha del camión.

17 x 6½ x 5 inches.   21 ozs.
430 x 165 x 125 mm.   595 gms.

11

MODERN MECHANICAL TOYS

REAL ACTION
MOTOR CYCLES
FITTED WITH PLATFORM FOR STANDING

No. 3148/1
MOTORCYCLE (Camouflaged).
MOTOCYCLETTE (Camouflé).
MOTOCICLETA (Disfrazado).
$5\frac{3}{4}$ x $1\frac{3}{4}$ x $3\frac{1}{4}$ inches.   3 ozs.
150 x 45 x 85 mm.   85 gms.

LIFELIKE IN EVERY DETAIL

No. 3149
MOTORCYCLE.
MOTOCYCLETTE.
MOTOCICLETA.
$7\frac{3}{4}$ x $2\frac{1}{2}$ x $4\frac{3}{4}$ inches. $3\frac{1}{2}$ ozs.
195 x 60 x 120 mm.   100 gms.

No. 3158
LARGE   ARMY   MOTORCYCLE
(Camouflaged).
MOTOCYCLETTE GRANDE
(Camouflé.)
MOTOCICLETA GRANDE
(Disfrazado).
$7\frac{1}{2}$ x $2\frac{1}{2}$ x $4\frac{3}{4}$ inches.   5 ozs.
190 x 60 x 120 mm.   140 gms.

12

REAL   ACTION   MOTOR   CYCLES

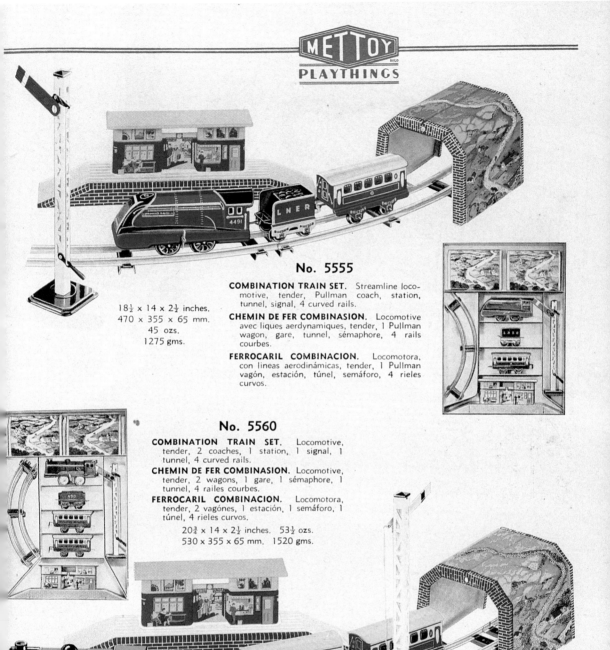

No. 5555

18½ x 14 x 2½ inches.
470 x 355 x 65 mm.
45 ozs.
1275 gms.

COMBINATION TRAIN SET. Streamline locomotive, tender, Pullman coach, station, tunnel, signal, 4 curved rails.

CHEMIN DE FER COMBINASION. Locomotive avec liques aerdynamiques, tender, 1 Pullman wagon, gare, tunnel, sémaphore, 4 rails courbes.

FERROCARIL COMBINACION. Locomotora, con lineas aerodinámicas, tender, 1 Pullman vagón, estación, túnel, semáforo, 4 rieles curvos.

No. 5560

COMBINATION TRAIN SET. Locomotive, tender, 2 coaches, 1 station, 1 signal, 1 tunnel, 4 curved rails.

CHEMIN DE FER COMBINASION. Locomotive, tender, 2 wagons, 1 gare, 1 sémaphore, 1 tunnel, 4 railes courbes.

FERROCARIL COMBINACION. Locomotora, tender, 2 vagónes, 1 estación, 1 semáforo, 1 túnel, 4 rieles curvos.

20¾ x 14 x 2½ inches. 53½ ozs.
530 x 355 x 65 mm. 1520 gms.

19

MODERN MECHANICAL TOYS

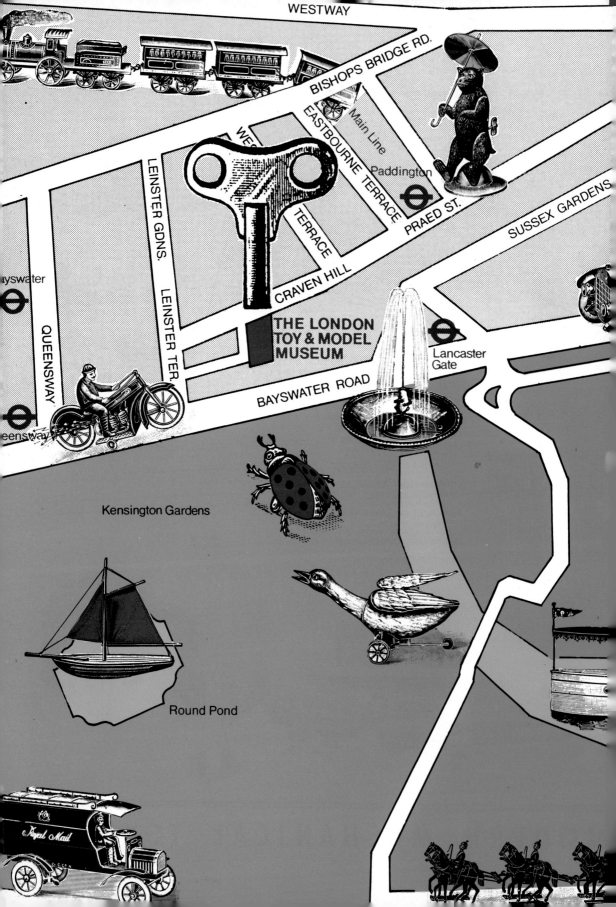

WESTWAY

BISHOPS BRIDGE RD.

WEST...

EASTBOURNE TERRACE

Main Line

Paddington

LEINSTER GDNS.

LEINSTER TER.

...TERRACE

CRAVEN HILL

PRAED ST.

SUSSEX GARDENS

Bayswater

QUEENSWAY

Queensway

THE LONDON TOY & MODEL MUSEUM

Lancaster Gate

BAYSWATER ROAD

Kensington Gardens

Round Pond

Royal Mail